THE TIME, SPACE & COST GUIDE
TO BETTER WAREHOUSE DESIGN

A hands-on guide to help you improve the design and operations of your warehouse or distribution center

Second Edition

Written by Maida Napolitano
and the Staff of Gross & Associates
167 Main Street
Woodbridge, NJ 07095
(732) 636-2666
www.GrossAssociates.com

Published by the Distribution Group
712 Main Street — Suite 187B
Boonton, NJ 07005-1450
(973) 265-2300
www.DistributionGroup.com

ISBN 978-0-915910-50-2
Library of Congress Catalog Card Number: 2003110552

CONTENTS

Chapter 1
Introduction . . . . .Page 1

Chapter 2
Warehouse Time Standards . . . . .Page 3

Chapter 3
Warehouse Space Calculations . . . . .Page 37

Chapter 4
Warehouse Cost Calculations . . . . .Page 89

Footnotes . . . . .Page 121

Bibliography . . . . .Page 123

Glossary . . . . .Page 133

LIST OF FIGURES

Figure 2.1	Sample of Labor Estimates Based on Time Standards	4
Figure 2.2	Comparing Alternatives Using Time Standards	6
Figure 2.3	Sample Comparison of Productivity Gains Before and After WMS and RF	7
Figure 2.4	Industry Throughput Standards	8
Figure 2.5	Summary of Time Standard Techniques	9
Figure 2.6	Sample Output of a Time Study on a Manual Batch Pick Operation	11
Figure 2.7	Sample Warehouse-Specific Activity Measurement Software	13
Figure 2.8	Steps for Establishing Warehouse Time Standards	15
Figure 2.9	Element-by-Element Breakdown of Pallet Putaway	16
Figure 2.10	Pallet Putaway Into Storage Area	18
Figure 2.11	Impact of Technology on Warehouse Time	20
Figure 2.12	Operation: Retrieving and Putting Away a Pallet Using a 24-Volt Narrow Aisle Reach Truck	21
Figure 2.13	Operation: Retrieving and Putting Away a Pallet Using a 36-Volt Narrow Aisle Reach Truck	22
Figure 2.14	Operation: Document Processing — Per Line Item Received	23
Figure 2.15	Operation: Document Processing — Checking Per Line Item Packed	24
Figure 2.16	Operation: Document Processing — Per Pallet Received or Shipped	24
Figure 2.17	Operation: Obtain and Operate Manual Pallet Jack	25
Figure 2.18	Operation: Turn Container (Slide)	25
Figure 2.19	Operation: Travel Times for Manual Pallet Jack	26

Figure 2.20   Operation: Package Handling — Mixed Loads   27

Figure 2.21   Operation: Package Handling — Solid Loads   28

Figure 2.22   Operation: Non-Powered Equipment and Pedestrian Travel Times   29

Figure 2.23   Operation: Lift Truck, Travel Into and Out of Trailer   30

Figure 2.24   Operation: Lift Truck (6000 Pounds)   30

Figure 2.25   Operation: Lift Truck (4000 Pounds, Electric), Travel with Pallet   31

Figure 2.26   Operation: Lift Truck (6000 Pounds, Electric), Travel with Pallet   31

Figure 2.27   Operation: Operate Lift Truck 1 (Electric)   31

Figure 2.28   Operation: Operate Lift Truck 2 (Electric)   32

Figure 2.29   Operation: Pallet, Load Into and Out of Trailer With Lift Truck   32

Figure 2.30   Operation: Material, Pick Up, Transport, Drop with Lift Truck   32

Figure 2.31   Operation: Unit Load Handling Times   33

Figure 2.32   Operation: Loading and Unloading Times   34

Figure 2.33   Operation: Assemble Carton   34

Figure 2.34   Operation: Push Cart (Loaded)   35

Figure 2.35   Miscellaneous Material Handling Standards   35

Figure 3.1   Sample Cross Dock Facility   38

Figure 3.2   Sample Storage Facility   39

Figure 3.3   General Approach to Warehouse Design   40

Figure 3.4   Product Flow Patterns   41

Figure 3.5   Comparison of Traditional and Modern Trailers   42

Figure 3.6   Sample Truck Apron Diagram   43

Figure 3.7   Sample Dock Leveler   45

Figure 3.8   Sample Truck Leveler   45

Figure 3.9   Mechanized Receiving with Elevated Sortation System   46

Figure 3.10   Sample Dock Layout with Staging Areas Defined   46

Figure 3.11   Safety Lip Truck Barrier   48

Figure 3.12   Various Ways of Placing Compactor on Dock   49

Figure 3.13   **Bin Drawers**   50

Figure 3.14   **Open Shelving**   50

Figure 3.15   **Mobile Shelving**   50

Figure 3.16   **Horizontal and Vertical Carousels**   51

Figure 3.17   **Cart, Hand Truck, and Platform Truck**   52

Figure 3.18   **Electric Sit-Down Counterbalanced Truck**   53

Figure 3.19   **Stand-Up Counterbalanced Truck**   53

Figure 3.20   **Walkie Stacker**   54

Figure 3.21   **Narrow Aisle Reach Truck**   54

Figure 3.22   **Operator-Up Turret (Swing Reach) Truck**   55

Figure 3.23   **Articulating Truck**   55

Figure 3.24   **Side-Loader Truck**   56

Figure 3.25   **Omni-Directional Truck**   56

Figure 3.26   **Relative Storage Height Capabilities of Lift Trucks**   57

Figure 3.27   **Material Handling Equipment and Appropriate Storage Module**   57

Figure 3.28   **Sample Inventory Profile and Corresponding Storage Modules**   61

Figure 3.29   **Sample Excess Inventory Analysis**   62

Figure 3.30   **Effects of Honeycombing**   63

Figure 3.31   **Calculating Effects of Honeycombing And Storage Utilization**   64

Figure 3.32   **Effects of Column Spacing**   65

Figure 3.33   **Optimal Column Spacing Example (Perpendicular to Aisles)**   66

Figure 3.34   **Optimal Column Spacing Example (Parallel to Aisles)**   66

Figure 3.35   **Trucks Versus Storage Modules**   67

Figure 3.36   **Comparison of Storage Densities**   68

Figure 3.37   **Pallet Storage Examples**   69

Figure 3.38   **Space Per Pallet Comparison**   69

Figure 3.39   **Design Year Inventory Profile**   70

Figure 3.40   **Generation of Storage Concepts**   72

Figure 3.41   **Space Requirements**   72

Figure 3.42   Handling Requirements   73

Figure 3.43   Pick-to-Light Modules   74

Figure 3.44   Picking from Pallet Flow Racks   74

Figure 3.45   Carousels with Pick-to-Light Technology   75

Figure 3.46   A-Frame — Automated Order Selection Device   76

Figure 3.47   Automated Full Case Order Selection System   76

Figure 3.48   Electric Pallet Truck   77

Figure 3.49   Orderpicker Truck   77

Figure 3.50   Single Order–Single Picker Diagram   79

Figure 3.51   Zone Pick Diagram   80

Figure 3.52   Batch Pick Diagram   80

Figure 3.53   Sample Full Case Movement Profile   84

Figure 3.54   Sample Full Case Popularity Profile   84

Figure 3.55   Various Picking Configurations   85

Figure 3.56   Order Picking Alternatives   86

Figure 3.57   Facings and Storage Capacity of Common Pick Modules   87

Figure 3.58   Piece-Pick, Pick-to-Tote Example With Case Flow Racks   87

Figure 4.1   Typical Building/Construction Costs   90

Figure 4.2   Location Factors   91

Figure 4.3   Material Handling Equipment Costs   93–95

Figure 4.4   Conveyor Systems Project Cost Breakdown   96

Figure 4.5   Storage Equipment Costs   97–100

Figure 4.6   Sample Planning and Design Costs   101

Figure 4.7   Dock Equipment Costs   103

Figure 4.8   Other Special Costs   104–105

Figure 4.9   A Worksheet for Calculating Costs of Ownership   106

Figure 4.10   Average Hourly Wages of Warehousing Jobs by Geographic Region and by Business   107

Figure 4.11   **Example of Annual Operating Expenses by Category
               for a Sample Warehouse**   111

Figure 4.12   **Interest Table to Determine the Capital Recovery Factor** 115

Figure 4.13   **Space and Handling Requirements for Case Study**   117

Figure 4.14   **Base Data**   117

Figure 4.15   **Investment Per Pallet Stored for Each Storage Concept**   118

Figure 4.16   **Generation of Final Alternatives**   119

Figure 4.17   **Economic Summary**   120

ABOUT THE AUTHOR

Maida Napolitano is a Senior Industrial Engineer with Gross & Associates. She is also the principal author for *Using Modeling to Solve Warehousing Problems* and *Making the Move to Cross Docking* (both published by the Warehousing Education and Research Council). She has worked for clients in the food, health care, retail, chemical, manufacturing, and cosmetics industries, primarily in the field of facility layout and planning, simulation, ergonomics, and statistical analysis. She holds BS and MS degrees in Industrial Engineering from the University of the Philippines and the New Jersey Institute of Technology, respectively.

Maida wishes to acknowledge the staff of Gross & Associates for their valuable assistance on this book. She extends a special thank you to: Bob Silverman, President of Gross & Associates; Don Derewecki, Executive Vice President; Jack Kuchta, Executive Vice President; Geoff Sisko, Executive Vice President; Todd Richter, Vice President Information Technology; Carlos Bastos, Director of Engineering; and Virginia Muller, Office Manager. A special thank you is extended to J. George Gross (retired) for his help in editing the contents. And to Troy Reynolds and Sarah Benardos of the Distribution Group for the painstaking editing and design of the book. She would also like to acknowledge the various equipment manufacturers who have contributed their product graphics and their expertise to this updated version. Contact information for these companies has been provided at the end of the book.

CHAPTER 1:
INTRODUCTION

The consequences of poor planning and design is often costly. Even small oversights, such as inadequately sized dock doors or improperly positioned rack beams, can snowball into large, head-pounding problems. The only way to avoid or counteract this downward spiral is by getting back to the basics: Reassess the current operation, then properly plan and design — or re-design — the facility to create a world-class warehouse.

How does one go about designing a world-class warehouse? Begin by understanding the qualities that make a warehouse world class. It must offer consistent high-quality service in a facility that is economical to build, efficient to operate, and flexible enough to adapt to changing business conditions. Its operational components must consist of a complex but balanced array of facility, people, equipment, information systems, and product, which work as a cohesive unit to maximize the utilization of space while optimizing throughput. It must also perform all of these tasks under an inflexible trio of constraints: limited time, finite available space, and bottom-line costs.

These dimensions of time, space, and costs are the three cornerstones by which an efficient and effective warehouse is measured. A warehouse that is able to accomplish its mission while saving time, space, and costs in the process is on its way to world-class status. Knowing how to use these measures in warehouse design becomes a definite advantage to a warehouse manager. It is also the primary subject of this book.

The chapter on warehouse time standards discusses the use of time to measure work, estimate labor requirements, evaluate alternative designs, improve operations and benchmark operations, as well as its use as input in simulation analysis. By measuring time in the warehouse, one can identify opportunities in the design where time can be saved, subsequently reducing labor costs and increasing throughput. This chapter also includes a collection of common warehouse time standards that can be used in planning and design.

The chapter on warehouse space calculations goes beyond just calculating space requirements for the different operational areas of a warehouse. It also includes an introduction to the basic components of warehouse space from the receiving to the shipping docks. It discusses how to design these functions in the least amount of space.

The chapter on warehouse cost calculations focuses on the conversion of time and space requirements into their bottom-line costs. It summarizes the different warehouse cost centers with the latest cost figures, spreadsheets, and techniques to analyze these costs. It also discusses how cost calculations are used to justify and evaluate alternative designs.

Throughout this book, the authors have made an effort to combine a theoretical yet practical approach that is applicable to both conventional and "state of the art" warehouses. The broad scope of information is useful to both experienced and inexperienced managers. For the experienced warehouse manager, this book will serve as a tool for improving productivity. It can also be used as a guide for preliminary design and operations analysis. This book will also acquaint the less experienced manager with the basics of warehousing.

Chapter 2
WAREHOUSE TIME STANDARDS

Work measurement is defined as the quantification of work units produced by one or more individuals and the comparison of these units to *objectively derived standards of performance* in order to assess efficiency.[1] When work is measured in units of time under normal working conditions, a *time standard*, also known as a *labor standard*, is established.

Although industrial engineers have touted its importance for more than a century, establishing time standards has had its share of controversy. Some experts argue that time standards tend to be *unrealistic, adversarial,* and *demoralizing* to workers.[2] Human beings come in all shapes and sizes, with each person working differently under varying conditions. The more variation in performing a task, the more difficult it is to establish a "realistic" standard time for that task. Some workers are wary and resent being timed. In one example, to avoid ruffling feathers, standards were set too low, and workers took their time after reaching the standards. Management was not happy that employees slackened off; in turn, workers lost respect for management.

But neglecting standards, especially in the labor-intensive world of material handling, warehousing, and distribution, can be foolhardy. Standards establish the length of time certain resources in the warehouse are dedicated to specific tasks. Not knowing elapsed times is akin to managing the warehouse in the dark.

How would you know how many pickers would be needed to select orders? How would you know how many lift trucks to use? How do you schedule receipts and shipments? How would you know how much time is saved in a new operation if you never measured how long it took doing it the old way? Sure, you could cross your fingers and hope everything works out. But wouldn't it be better to study each operation and determine how much time it takes?

As a productivity tool, a fair and realistic standard allows management to tell workers exactly what is expected of them. When workers fall below standards, it alerts management to potential barriers to productivity that should be rectified.

In warehouse design, time standards enable you to determine with a level of accuracy the number of workers and the amount of equipment required to run the warehouse during average and peak times. For a new operation, using standards can help you determine how many work stations will be needed, how many people will be required, and how much equipment should be purchased. For third-party warehouse managers, standards help estimate costs for prospective clients.

In this chapter, we explore the use of time standards in warehousing with special emphasis on designing warehouses. First, we discuss their applications in the warehouse; then, we list the different methods for establishing standards. The subjects of time standards and work measurement are well documented. In this book, general issues are discussed without delving into complex statistical analyses, which is often required for accurate time studies. For more detailed discussions, refer to the bibliography at the end of the book.

Applications of Time Standards in Warehousing

A warehouse manager can use time standards in a variety of applications and in virtually any type of working environment. Some of these applications are explained below.

1. Estimating Labor Requirements. Estimating the labor requirements to run a warehouse can be a daunting task. **Figure 2.1** demonstrates this application for a typical warehouse. The time study analyst must first isolate and determine the job functions to be estimated. Next, standards must be determined for each function. In this case, predetermined time standards were used. Once established, each standard was multiplied by the average volume for every function. Dividing this number by the available working hours will determine the labor required.

Figure 2.1. Sample of Labor Estimates Based on Time Standards

Function[1]	Time Standard (Minutes)	Daily Volume Per Function	Total Time Based on Volume (Minutes)	Estimated People Required[2]
Pallet putaway	3.3	13 pallets	42.9	0.1
Replenishment operations				
Replenish full case pick modules	32.9	8 "mixed pallets"	263.2	0.6
Replenish broken case pick modules	24.6	2 "mixed pallets"	49.2	0.1
Order-picking operations				
Full case picks	1.4	5,863 orders	8,208.2	18.2
Broken case picks	6.7	398 orders	2,666.6	5.9
Manual packing operations	1.4	398 orders	557.2	1.2
Pallet staging	5.4	21 "mixed pallets"	113.4	0.3
Total people required at average throughput capacity:				26.4

[1] The following list includes only those operations involved in directly handling the product.

[2] Total people required is based on a 7.5-hour (450-minute) workday.

2. Scheduling Jobs and the Workforce. Determining time standards for each operation will also help in scheduling jobs and allocating the workforce. Knowing the time it takes to perform all operations, the manager can allocate workers in advance to utilize them better and to reduce idle worker time.

3. Providing Measures of Productivity. The performance index, one of many measures of productivity, bases its calculations on time standards. The number of pieces or jobs that the worker finishes daily is multiplied by the standard time to finish a piece or job. The performance index is the ratio of the total standard time to the actual number of available labor hours.

$$\text{Performance Index} = \frac{\text{Pieces Finished} \times \text{Standard Time/Piece}}{\text{Available Labor Hours}}$$

For example: If the standard time to repackage a perfume bottle in a returns processing area is 0.23 min, a worker who finishes 1,990 pieces in a 7.5-hour workday has the following performance index:

$$\text{Performance Index} = \frac{1,990 \text{ Pieces} \times 0.23 \text{ Minutes/Piece}}{450 \text{ Minutes}} = 1.02 = 102\%$$

A performance index of less than 100% means the worker has worked below the standard rate. The reduced productivity should be investigated. *Although useful for tracking worker performance, the predetermined time standards in this publication are not recommended for establishing wage incentive programs without doing a detailed time study under actual warehouse conditions.*

4. Evaluating Alternative Operations. Another effective application of using standards is to evaluate alternative methods of performing warehousing tasks. For example, company ABC wants to determine the feasibility of replacing its fleet of manual pallet jacks with electric pallet jacks for picking orders. The difference between alternatives is in the travel time. **Figure 2.2** shows the incremental difference in travel time between both alternatives. (In this case, predetermined time standards established by the Department of Defense were used.)

Totaling the time values shows that using electric pallet jacks can save almost three minutes in picking every order. For the total of a day's orders and assuming one order per trip, the total travel time is:

Manual Pallet Jack: 400 trips x 5.44 minutes/trip = 2,176 man-mins = 36.3 manhours

Electric Pallet Jack: 400 trips x 2.64 minutes/trip = 1,056 man-mins = 17.6 manhours

Using electric pallet jacks would save 18.7 manhours daily, or 2.5 people based on a 7.5-hour workday. With an annual salary of $28,000 per operator, using electric pallet jacks results in

Figure 2.2. Comparing Alternatives Using Time Standards

| | | | Total Time (Minutes) | |
| | | | Manual Pallet Jack | Electric Pallet Jack |
	Element Description	Frequency of Moves		
1	Travel to empty pallet stack. Average distance: 120 feet (includes start, accelerate, move, and one turn)	1	0.530	0.418
2	Pick up empty pallet (includes turning 90 degrees to change direction of travel)	1	0.115	0.034
3	Travel to picking locations			
	To 1st pick location: 80 feet, one turn into picking aisle	1	0.313	0.274
	Case pick time (4 pick locations)	4	same	same
	To 2nd pick location: 100 feet, four turns into picking aisle	1	0.662	0.346
	To 3rd pick location: 20 feet, two turns into picking aisle	1	0.293	0.097
	To 4th pick location: 50 feet, no (0) turns into picking aisle	1	0.312	0.223
	For manual jacks only: (for 33% of picks)			
	Obtain and position ladder	0.33	0.288	na
	Climb up steps to pick cartons	same	same	same
	Return ladder	0.33	0.257	na
	For electric jacks only:			
	Mount/dismount pallet jack	4	na	0.095
4	Travel to staging area. Travel distance: 200 feet (2 turns-loaded)	1	1.244	0.517
5	Drop pallet in staging area	1	0.516	0.294
	Subtotal:		4.530	2.298
	Personal fatigue and delay allowance (20% for manual, 15% for powered jacks):		0.906	0.345
	Grand total (travel minutes/order):		5.436	2.643

Assumptions:

1 All turns are 90 degrees.

2 A single order is picked per trip. Product is picked from two levels of the storage rack.

3 Electric pallet jack is equipped with a step.

Source: *Standardization of Work Measurement* (Volume X). Department of Defense, 1977.

Figure 2.3. Sample Comparison of Productivity Gains Before and After WMS and RF

Before WMS and RF:

Element Description of Pallet Replenishment of Pick Facings	Average Time (sec)	Frequency	Total Time (sec)
Record locations to be replenished	7.0	23%	1.6
Look up locations	7.6	58%	4.4
Travel to withdrawal location	19.1	100%	19.1
Withdraw pallet	26.0	100%	26.0
Travel to deposit location	18.3	100%	18.3
Remove shrink/wrap pallets	15.8	19%	3.0
Deposit pallet	6.1	100%	6.1
Pick large quantity for picker	23.0	15%	3.5
Record moves	6.3	81%	5.1
Align loads	18.0	4%	0.7
Subtotal time:			87.8
Personal fatigue and delay allowance:		15%	13.2
Grand total:			101.0
Net pallets per hour: 28.2			

After WMS and RF:

Element Description of Pallet Replenishment of Pick Facings	Average Time (sec)	Frequency	Total Time (sec)
Travel to withdrawal location	15.3	100%	15.3
Scan pallet barcode	3.0	100%	3.0
Withdraw pallet	26.0	100%	26.0
Travel to deposit location	18.3	100%	18.3
Remove shrink/wrap pallets	15.8	19%	3.0
Scan location barcode	3.0	100%	3.0
Deposit pallet	6.1	100%	6.1
Pick large quantity for picker	23.0	15%	3.5
Align loads	18.0	4%	0.7
Subtotal time:			78.9
Personal fatigue and delay allowance:		15%	11.8
Grand total:			90.7
Net pallets per hour: 31.4			
Productivity gained: 11%			

Radio frequency data collection can potentially increase net pallets per hour in warehouse replenishment operations. Workers are directed intelligently, manual look-up is eliminated, and customer orders suffer fewer stockouts. Source: Trunk, Christopher, "Warehouse Management Systems: New Pathways to Justification," *Material Handling Engineering*, Jan. 1998, p. 52. Copyright Penton Media Inc., Cleveland, OH. All rights reserved.

base pay savings of approximately $70,000 per year. Currently, company ABC uses 15 pickers with manual pallet jacks to pick full case orders. Using electric pallet jacks, picking could be done by 13 pickers. The capital cost of 13 electric pallet jacks is $117,000 at $9,000 each. With the annual savings of $70,000, the payback period would be 1.7 years. This type of analysis facilitates management's decision-making process.

Figure 2.3 is another example of comparing alternatives to determine the productivity gained before and after using a warehouse management system (WMS) and radio frequency (RF) technology. In a typical RF installation, wireless terminals are installed on lift trucks to communicate directly to the host computer from the warehouse floor. RF creates a paperless work environment where the information required to perform a task is transmitted in real time to the worker's terminal. This eliminates manual recording and referencing putaway and replenishment locations. With RF, the information is at the driver's fingertips. For this sample study, using RF and WMS has increased the number of pallets replenished by about 11% per hour.

5. Improving Warehouse Operations. With an element-by-element breakdown of a task, establishing time standards requires the analyst to scrutinize any task and perform a methods study. Barriers to productivity can then be determined. For example, a time study analysis showed a receiving lift truck operator spending an inordinate amount of time walking back and forth to the warehouse office to process an inbound load. Placing a terminal on the receiving dock reduced this wasted time as a "quick fix." Long term, management installed a wireless RF terminal onboard the lift truck, thus also eliminating the time spent dismounting and mounting the vehicle.

6. Providing Real Time Values For Simulation Analysis. A more technical application of time standards can be found in simulation analysis. Simulation is an analytical tool that

Figure 2.4. Industry Throughput Standards

Warehouse Activity	Per Person		Units
	Lower Range	Upper Range	
Lift Truck Pallet Movement			
Counter-balance	12	20	pallets/hour
Narrow aisle reach	12	18	pallets/hour
Man-up turret	15	25	pallets/hour
Man-down turret	15	25	pallets/hour
Narrow aisle articulating	12	18	pallets/hour
Order Picking (Cases)			
Pick-to-powered pallet jack	30	80	lines/hour
	100	200	cases/hour
Man-up orderpicker truck	20	60	lines/hour
	50	100	cases/hour
Case pick to conveyor	200	400	cases/hour
Order Picking (Pieces)			
Pick-to-cart	30	100	lines/hour
Carousel-to-container	200	400	lines/hour
Flow rack-to-container	100	200	lines/hour
Bin shelves-to-container	60	150	lines/hour
Truck Load/Unload			
Unload floor to conveyor	200	400	cartons/hour
Handstack into trailers	100	250	cartons/hour
Palletizing from Conveyor	150	350	cartons/hour

Note: These rates are broad estimates based on experience in a wide variety of applications. There are many variables that must be considered, such as product slotting; travel distances; the use of paper-, RF-, or voice-directed activities; training; the opportunity to dual cycle; the ability to carry multiple pallets in a move; etc.

enables the user to mathematically model an operation on a computer before physically implementing it. Statistical distributions of different parameters, such as arrival rates of trucks, profiles of orders, picking times, etc., provide the data to run the simulation. To be close to reality, time standards of basic elements are used to provide the time value as input for the simulation.

7. Comparing Present Standards Against Established Industry Standards. Finally, if the time standard has been determined for an operation, a manager can compare that standard with a predetermined time standard for a particular operation. The critical point to remember in comparing standards is that actual times may vary significantly depending upon factors which include the type of warehouse, the product handled, the physical environment, the frequency of operations, and the actual distance traveled during each operation. Nevertheless, standards do provide benchmarks to compare present productivity levels. **Figure 2.4** shows some samples of throughput standards in the warehouse compiled by the authors.

Time Standard Techniques

There are four techniques for developing time standards: through time study, from predetermined time standards, from work or activity sampling, or from historical data. **Figure 2.5** summarizes these techniques.

1. Time Study. This is the most widely used tool for developing standard times. Times are determined from actual stopwatch timing of an operation. A stopwatch time standard is estab-

Figure 2.5. Summary of Time Standard Techniques

Technique	Description	Recommended Application	Propensity for Methods Improvement	Worker Involvement	Skill Level Requirements	Accuracy
Time Study	Break down of tasks into small elements that can be readily timed	• Short, repetitive, highly variable tasks • Recommended for incentive wage programs	High	High	High	High
Predetermined Time Standards	Collection of ready-made time values without need for timing	• Short cycle, highly repetitive tasks • New operations • Good for labor estimates, alternative analysis • Third-party warehouse cost estimation	High	None	Medium	Medium to High
Work or Activity Sampling	Random observations of workers' busy and idle time	• Long cycle, highly variable tasks • Recommended for determination of idle time	Low	Low	Low	Low to Medium
Historical Data	Use of job records or productivity logs	• Long cycle, highly variable tasks • Accuracy for warehousing increases with radio frequency and WMS support	Low	None	Low	Low to Medium

lished by breaking down the operation into small elements that can be readily timed. Allowances for working conditions, personal needs, fatigue, and delays beyond the worker's control are factored into the standardized time for that operation. The old method was to use the stopwatch and clipboard system with manual data transfer and analysis. This has been replaced by handheld, touchscreen computers that perform time studies with hundredths of a second precision and can be downloaded to the computer or PC. An icon represents the task element on the handheld computer screen. The analyst touches the icon at the beginning and end of the element, while sometimes continuing observations for the next element. In complex operations, eliminating the need to read the watch and record the time on paper speeds up the time study and reduces the number of iterations an analyst has to observe in order to get real times. Entry error from the manual transfer of data to a PC is eliminated as raw data can be saved automatically to the PC. The software can immediately provide the statistical analysis of the process.

Time studies are especially useful for short, repetitive, highly variable tasks. They are recommended in incentive wage programs where specific working conditions are required. Although popular, the time study method is subjective and relies heavily on the skill and experience of the analyst who needs to determine where the worker fits on a scale, with 100 percent being average. Some workers become uncomfortable when followed and timed. There are also concerns that only a small percentage of the workforce will meet the average time for performing tasks. To meet these issues, analysts are trained to exercise good judgment and use statistics to validate the accuracy of the studies.[3]

Figure 2.6 illustrates a sample time study of a batch picking operation in a third-party warehouse. Management of this third-party warehouse wanted a formula to show prospective clients the estimates of how long it would take to batch pick a group of orders. The exercise is for the picker to assemble the required number of cartons for a batch of orders in a pick trolley and pick the required number of pieces of each stockkeeping unit (SKU) for all the orders in the batch. In this exercise, picking the orders had both constant and variable time elements that were dependent on the number of locations the picker had to visit and the number of orders in the batch. Here, averages are used for simplicity. The formula per batch of orders was determined to be:

2.46 min + (1.44 min x Locations Picked) + (1.22 min x Orders In Batch)

Thus, for a batch of 20 orders involving 10 SKUs, it would take one person an average of 41.26 minutes, or 2.46 min + (1.44 min x 10) + (1.22 min x 20), to piece-pick a batch of orders.

2. Predetermined Time Standards. A predetermined time standard system is a collection of ready-made time values for basic motion elements. This includes predetermined motion time systems (PMTS), which were originally developed by experienced analysts who agreed on certain basic factors, concepts, and constraints underlying their system. Methods-time measurement (MTM), the work factor system (WFS), and dimensional motion times (DMT) are some examples of PMTS. The use of PMTS requires the analyst to break down a task into detailed motions.

Figure 2.6. Sample Output of a Time Study on a Manual Batch Pick Operation

Client Name: Company ZYX
Date: Month, day, year
Operator: Multiple

Operation: Order picking
Starts: Picker picks up combined pick list (CPL)
Ends: Picker signs out

Time Analyst: Carlos
Sheet No: 1 of 1
Equipment: Pick trolley

	1	2	3	4	5	6	7	8	9	10	Average
Cycle Start Time	8:15:00 AM	11:15:00 AM	8:45:00 AM	11:05:00 AM	8:26:00 AM	8:35:00 AM	10:48:00 AM	9:26:00 AM	9:50:00 AM	2:56:00 PM	
Cycle End Time	8:50:20 AM	11:30:49 AM	8:49:28 AM	11:24:46 AM	8:35:29 AM	8:57:06 AM	10:58:28 AM	9:46:35 AM	10:13:12 AM	3:08:31 PM	

Observed Cycles (minutes)

Element #	Element Description	1	2	3	4	5	6	7	8	9	10	Average
1	Picks up CPL and order forms	00:15	00:20	00:20	00:10	00:15	00:10	00:25	00:10	00:15	00:20	00:16
2	Signs out on job labor card	00:15	00:10	00:20	00:30	00:20	00:15	00:20	00:15	00:10	00:15	00:17
3	Goes to empty shipping cartons	00:18	00:10	00:15	00:05	00:10	00:15	00:10	00:30	00:22	00:17	00:15
4	Gets shipping cartons for each order	00:45	00:30	00:10	00:50	00:35	00:40	00:10	00:21	00:30	00:45	00:32
5	Total for travel to pick locations	27:12	09:53	00:55	12:30	06:04	16:14	04:50	10:45	13:45	05:56	10:48
6	Total for picks of pieces for each order	04:00	02:36	00:40	03:20	00:30	02:25	02:35	06:20	05:40	02:46	03:05
7	Pushes cart to packing table	01:20	01:00	01:20	01:11	01:00	01:20	00:55	01:10	01:20	01:03	01:10
8	Checks off each order quantity	00:30	00:15		00:10				00:30	00:30	00:20	00:19
9	Signs order form if order is complete	00:20	00:10	00:03	00:16	00:10	00:10	00:10	00:10	00:15	00:12	00:12
10	Walks to desk, signs, and drops off CPL	00:15	00:25	00:15	00:20	00:15	00:12	00:28	00:14	00:15	00:25	00:18
11	Signs out on job labor card	00:10	00:20	00:10	00:24	00:10	00:15	00:15	00:10	00:10	00:12	00:14
	Total Time	35:20	15:49	04:28	19:46	09:29	22:06	10:28	20:35	23:12	12:31	17:22

Batch Properties

	1	2	3	4	5	6	7	8	9	10	
No. of locations picked per CPL	15	8	1	7	4	1	3	6	7	4	
No. of orders completed	3	3	1	4	1	2	3	7	6	3	

Elements (minutes)

Element #	Element Description	1	2	3	4	5	6	7	8	9	10	Average
1,2,3,7,10,11	Constant time per CPL (order batch)	02:33	02:25	02:40	02:40	02:10	02:27	02:33	02:29	02:32	02:32	02:30
5	Time for all pick locations	27:12	09:53	00:55	12:30	06:04	16:14	04:50	10:45	13:45	05:56	10:48
4,6,8,9	Time for all orders completed	05:35	03:31	00:53	04:36	01:15	03:25	03:05	07:21	6:55	04:03	4:04

Time Per Unit of Measure (minutes)

	1	2	3	4	5	6	7	8	9	10	Average
Constant time per CPL (order batch)	02:33	02:25	02:40	02:10	02:10	02:27	02:33	02:29	02:32	02:32	02:30
Time per pick location (line on CPL)	01:49	01:14	00:55	01:47	01:31	01:48	01:37	01:47	01:58	01:29	01:36
Time per order	01:52	01:10	00:53	01:09	01:15	01:42	01:02	01:03	01:09	01:21	01:16

Performance Rating

	1	2	3	4	5	6	7	8	9	10	Average
	85%	102%	120%	95%	88%	85%	105%	90%	95%	95%	96%

Adjusted Time Per Unit of Measure (minutes)

		1	2	3	4	5	6	7	8	9	10	Average	PF&D Allowances	Standard Time
A	Constant time per CPL (order batch)	02:10	02:28	03:12	02:32	01:54	02:05	02:41	02:14	02:24	02:24	02:24	15%	02:46 min.
B	Time per pick location (line on CPL)	01:32	01:16	01:06	01:42	01:20	01:32	01:41	01:37	01:25	01:25	01:30	15%	01:44 min.
C	Time per order	01:35	01:12	01:04	01:06	01:06	01:27	01:05	00:57	01:17	01:17	01:11	15%	01:22 min.

Formula per batch of orders: A + (B x Locations Picked) + (C x Orders in Batch) = 2.46 min + (1.44 min x Locations Picked)+(1.22 min x Orders in Batch).

Source: *Using Modeling to Solve Warehousing Problems*, by Maida Napolitano and Gross & Associates. Copyright 1998 Warehousing Education and Research Council, Oakbrook, IL. All rights reserved.

Most PMTS have been computerized by vendors and are now part of large, often expensive standards management software.[4]

The disadvantage of some of these systems is that they tend to study manufacturing more and warehousing less, and they are crammed with too much detail, dealing with micro-motion analyses such as left-hand, right-hand motion. Other predetermined time standards are set by the warehouse industry or by warehouse equipment manufacturers. Some consultants have created databases of warehousing standards collected onsite from previous clients or developed from PMTS. **Figure 2.7** shows sample screens from work measurement software that uses an interactive menu and a considerable database of predetermined time standards to develop times and their associated labor and equipment costs for a wide range of warehousing jobs. Some material handling equipment manufacturers also keep a record of standards for in-house use. The Department of Defense has a collection of material handling standards — many archaic, some of which are still relevant — that can be used to measure work. Samples of these standards are listed at the end of this chapter.

Predetermined time standards are especially useful for new operations where there are no precedents by which tasks can be measured. Thus, they are most useful in designing new warehouse operations. Third-party warehouse managers use this technique to develop costs for prospective clients. There is no stopwatch timing, and it is not intrusive to workers. It is recommended for short-cycle, highly repetitive tasks.

3. Work or Activity Sampling. Work sampling is based upon the laws of probability; that is, a sample taken at random from a large set tends to have the same pattern of distribution as the larger group or universe.[5] In a simple work sampling study, an analyst records whether workers are working or idle at random times during the day. The proper size of the sample is calculated based on a predetermined degree of accuracy. After the number of sample observations is completed, the percentage of time that workers are idle and busy is calculated as follows:

$$\text{Working Time (in percent)} = \frac{\text{Number of Observations Working}}{\text{Total Observations}}$$

$$\text{Idle Time (in percent)} = \frac{\text{Number of Observations Idle}}{\text{Total Observations}}$$

For example, assume a lift truck driver works an 8-hour day, or 480 minutes, moving pallets from receiving to shipping in a cross dock operation. A work sampling study included 640 observations. Sixty-two (62) observations showed he was idle. Thus, 10 percent of the time he is considered to be idle ($62 \div 640 = 10\%$). The remaining 578 observations showed he was working. Thus, 90 percent of the time he is considered to be working or busy ($578 \div 640 = 90\%$). His average performance index has been observed to be 20% above the standard, or

Figure 2.7. Sample Warehouse-Specific Activity Measurement Software

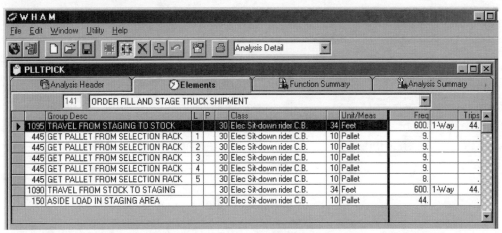

Shows the elements involved in the function, Order Fill and Stage Truck Shipment, along with the frequency of occurrence for each element.

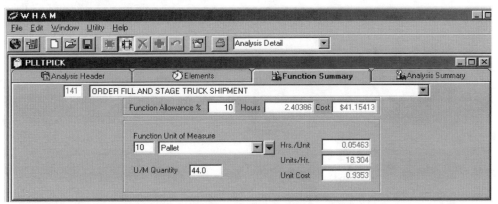

Shows the final time value of the functions as calculated from the previous screen. An allowance of 10% is used to compensate for employee fatigue and miscellaneous delays. The software then allows the user to calculate different units of measure.

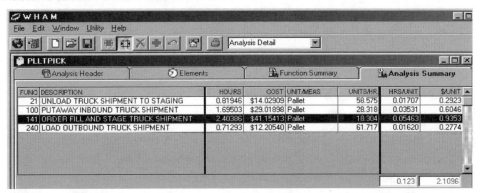

Shows the analysis summary, which brings together the calculations for time and cost for all the functions being analyzed.

Reprinted with permission from Consulting Services Company, a Division of Bohm Company, Chicago, IL.

120%. A personal fatigue allowance is set at 15%. WMS records show he moved 75 pallets. The standard time per pallet can be calculated as follows using the sample data provided[6]:

Information	Source of Data	Output for the Day
Total time of lift truck driver (Working time + idle time)	WMS	480 minutes
Total pallets moved	WMS	75 pallets
Working time in percent	Work sampling	90%
Idle time in percent	Work sampling	10%
Average performance index (API)	Work sampling	120%
Total allowances	Time study-set	15%

$$\text{Standard Time Per Pallet} = \frac{(\text{Total Time}) \times (\text{Working Time \%}) \times \text{API}}{\text{Number of Pallets Moved Per Day}} \times \frac{100}{100 - \text{Allow}} =$$

$$= \frac{(480 \times 0.90 \times 1.20)}{75} \times \frac{100}{100-15} = 8.08 \text{ Min Per Pallet}$$

Work sampling can establish standard times on highly variable and long cycle tasks, where people are employed in groups and the tasks do not lend themselves to lengthy time studies. Although work sampling isolates delays, or idle time, from busy time, it does not provide the analyst with more information to determine the cause of such delays since activities are not broken down into smaller elements. Conversely, work sampling is considered to be less "invasive" to workers as compared to an actual time study where the worker is under observation for continuous periods of time.

4. Historical Data. The use of historical data is considered to be a more educated but less engineered technique for establishing time standards. It is most useful when accurate job records are kept. The use of RF technology and WMS that track each worker's action on the warehouse floor has made it easier to measure work based on actual performance. Some systems begin tracking task time as soon as the lift truck operator is directed to his next task and end when he scans a pallet to signify completion of the task. Experts recommend the use of a moving average to set the standard time because methods change and the standard time gradually changes with each new historical data point.

In historical data, as in work sampling, the total elapsed time does not isolate delays or problems that may be apparent in an element-by-element breakdown of a task. The use of historical data is especially useful in establishing a baseline standard for a current operation that is being improved. It takes the least time and effort to gather raw data, especially where the WMS can provide detailed labor reports.

Steps for Establishing Warehouse Time Standards

In this section, we detail the steps for developing warehouse time standards using predetermined time standards and actual time studies. **Figure 2.8** summarizes these steps.

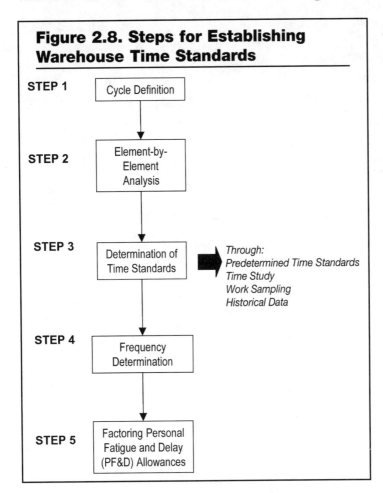

Figure 2.8. Steps for Establishing Warehouse Time Standards

STEP 1 — Cycle Definition

STEP 2 — Element-by-Element Analysis

STEP 3 — Determination of Time Standards → Through: Predetermined Time Standards, Time Study, Work Sampling, Historical Data

STEP 4 — Frequency Determination

STEP 5 — Factoring Personal Fatigue and Delay (PF&D) Allowances

Step 1. Cycle Definition. The first step in developing time standards for an operation is to define the cycle. A cycle is the finite period of time with distinct start and end points within which a series of basic motion elements is performed. An example is the putaway of a pallet from the receiving dock into storage. The cycle could start with the operator obtaining the pallet at the receiving dock and end with the operator returning to the dock for the next pallet. Smaller cycles may also exist within a cycle. However, the analyst must pay careful attention to the frequency of occurrences, so as not to double count any operations. In the following example of a typical putaway operation, suppose that a cycle is a day's worth of work. A regular workday starts when the operator mounts a fully charged truck at the battery charging area and ends when the operator dismounts from the truck after putting away a day's worth of pallets.

Step 2. Element-by-Element Analysis. The next critical step is the breakdown of the procedure into simple, definable elements. These elements are usually groups of the basic motions that are long enough to be conveniently timed. **Figure 2.9** shows the breakdown of the elements in the putaway operation.

Step 3. Determination of Time Standards. The third step is to determine time standards for each element in the operation. The previous section explained the techniques for developing time standards. For this exercise, we concentrate on two ways: (1) using predetermined time standards or (2) time studies or actual stopwatch timing.

Predetermined time standards provide a quick but reliable measurement of previously

Figure 2.9. Element-by-Element Breakdown of Pallet Putaway

Operation: Pallet putaway into the storage area
Starts: Operator mounts truck in battery charging area
Ends: Operator dismounts truck in battery charging area[1]

Element Description
Mount/dismount reach truck

Travel from battery charging to palletizing station – empty
     Truck speed: 444 fpm[2]
     Travel distance: 435.5 ft

Obtain pallet at palletizing station
Read putaway directions on RF terminal

Travel to location from palletizing station – loaded
     Truck speed: 380 fpm[2]
     Travel distance: 98 ft

Vertical travel at putaway location – loaded
     Truck speed: 50.4 fpm[2]
     Travel distance: 11.5 ft

Insert pallet in rack

Lower forks at putaway location – empty
     Truck speed: 64 fpm[2]
     Travel distance: 11.5 ft

Travel to palletizing station – empty   Travel distance: 98 ft
Travel to battery charging from putaway   Travel distance: 335.5 ft

Assumptions:

[1] At the end of the day, operator returns truck to battery charging area for recharging.

[2] Based on a manufacturer's specifications of a reach truck.

observed task times without the need for additional stopwatch timing. Elements are classified as basic (single element) and extended (combinations of elements). These are the common building blocks that can be used to create a "local finite standard," which reflects the actual conditions found at a particular location. When average occurrences, densities, and prevalent distances are used, that standard is more aptly called a "gross measurement standard." In our example, time standards for basic and extended elements were selected from tables developed by the Department of Defense and various material handling consultants.

Sometimes an operation or an element in an operation may be unique, and therefore it is impossible to apply predetermined time standards. Perhaps certain critical conditions or special equipment are involved. Then, an analyst may need to conduct a *time study*. In a time study, a sample of stopwatch measurements must be collected and a representative value, usually the average, determined for each element in the operation. Before timing a worker, the analyst should consider the following key conditions:

- if the person has only recently learned the operation,

- if the method of doing the job has changed recently,

- if a person is experiencing temporary physiological impairments,

- if the equipment and product specifications have been altered, and

- if the physical working conditions have changed.

Factors are applied to account for the above conditions for each set of sample stopwatch measurements obtained for each worker. These are different from allowances that are added for personal fatigue and delay. Deciding the number of samples required for a time study is an exercise in statistical analysis. The more samples taken, the more typical will be the standard. To know if enough stopwatch measurements have been taken, use the following formula to allow for a 95% confidence level and precision to within 5%. N´ is the number of allowable samples that achieve 95% confidence level.

$$N' = \left(\frac{40\sqrt{N\sum x^2 - (\sum x)^2}}{\sum x} \right)^2$$

where,

x = Sample Times

N = Total Number of Samples

$\sum x$ = $x_1 + x_2 + ... + x_N$

= Total of Sample Times

$\sum x^2$ = $x_1^2 + x_2^2 + ... + x_N^2$

= Total of Sample Times Squared

Step 4. Frequency Determination. The next step is to determine the frequencies of occurrences for each element in the operation. It is largely dependent on the volume and throughput level at which the warehouse operates. By identifying and defining these parameters, an accurate and reliable measurement can be obtained and customized to the specific environment. In this example, the warehouse receives and stores a total of 225 pallets per day.

Step 5. Factoring Personal Fatigue and Delay (PF&D) Allowances. The total time standard of all the basic and extended elements provided either by time studies or predetermined time standards does not include allowances for personal fatigue and delay. This allowance factor accounts for the percentage of time that the worker is unable to continue at a normal pace because of personal and physiological reasons, such as fatigue, restroom breaks, etc. Standards established in other studies can be used. This includes 5% for personal rest plus allowances for fatigue based on the fatigue factor inherent in doing a given task. This factor may be only 5% for light work but 17% for heavy work. **Figure 2.10** shows the completed time standard analysis of the putaway of pallets into storage.

Once the extended data element incorporating travel time has been established as a local standard, it need not be checked again unless distances between source and destination points change. Some standard data for certain elements may have direct applications, while others may require adjustments due to frequency of occurrences, distance, weight, etc.

A computerized spreadsheet program will help keep track of data elements. The format for the time standard spreadsheet should identify the operation and the date it is analyzed, note if it is an existing or proposed condition, define the cycle, and state the working assumptions.

Figure 2.10. Pallet Putaway Into Storage Area

Operation: Pallet putaway into the storage area
Starts: Operator mounts truck in battery charging area
Ends: Operator dismounts truck in battery charging area[1]

Procedure: Existing
Filename: Putaway.xls
Date: 00-00-00

Daily Pallets From In-plant Production Facility: 225 Pallets

Element Description	Frequency Minutes	Number of Moves	Total Minutes
1 Mount/dismount reach truck	0.226	2	0.452

2 Travel from battery charging to palletizing station – empty
    Truck speed: 444 fpm[2]
    Travel distance: 435.5 ft
	0.981	1	0.981

3 Obtain pallet at palletizing station	0.279	225	62.775
4 Read putaway directions on RF terminal	0.116	225	26.100

5 Travel to location from palletizing station – loaded
    Truck speed: 380 fpm[2]
    Travel distance: 98 ft
	0.258	225	58.050

6 Vertical travel at putaway location – loaded
    Truck speed: 50.4 fpm[2]
    Travel distance: 11.5 ft
	0.228	225	51.300

7 Insert pallet in rack	0.279	225	62.775

8 Lower forks at putaway location – empty
    Truck speed: 64 fpm[2]
    Travel distance: 11.5 ft
	0.180	225	40.500

9 Travel to palletizing station – empty Travel distance: 98 ft	0.221	224	49.504
10 Travel to battery charging from putaway Travel distance: 335.5 ft	0.756	1	0.756
Subtotal:			353.193
15% personal fatigue and delay allowance:			52.979
Total time daily:			406.172

Total manpower[3]: 406.172 min/450 min = 0.902, or 1 person

Assumptions:
[1] At the end of the day, operator returns truck to battery charging area for recharging.
[2] Based on a manufacturer's specifications of a reach truck.
[3] Based on an average workday of 7.5 hours, or 450 minutes.

Technology's Impact on Warehouse Time

Rapid advancements in computer and communications technology have been revving up the speed of operations in the warehouse. Only a decade or so ago, orders would come in by fax, and then they would sit at someone's desk until somebody found the time to punch it into the system. Just a few years ago, it wasn't surprising to see pickers walking all over the warehouse with paper pick lists looking for that hard-to-find item. Things have changed. Orders that used to take days can now be processed in hours. Pickers that used to take hours can complete tasks in minutes. Time in the warehouse seems to have shrunk, and technology is the culprit.

Radio frequency-directed warehousing, pick-to-light technology, computer-to-computer communication, voice recognition systems, infrared sensors, and highly versatile warehouse management systems are just some of the technology that has changed the face of warehousing. **Figure 2.11** shows how these systems have impacted the time it takes to process orders and improved warehouse productivity.

Consider the evolution of the process for filling an order. Time used to be spent reading pick lists, finding the proper location, then reading on paper the quantity that must be picked. Now, radio frequency technology is used to direct pickers. The barcodes on pick locations and products are scanned to verify a pick. With pick-to-light technology, pick modules are fitted with LED lights that guide pickers to pick locations and display how much to pick. A picker pushes a button to verify a pick. Even the 1 to 2 seconds of pushing this button has been eliminated in some cases with the use of infrared sensors mounted on pick faces. The picker breaking the beam with his hand indicates that a pick is made. All of these technological enhancements have one primary goal in mind — to reduce the time it takes to pick an order.

Using the latest warehousing tools further emphasizes the need to closely analyze how much time you spend on your operation. Creating time standards will quantify the time saved. Time saved is money saved. It is these savings that will allow you to justify these capital-intensive technological enhancements.

A Last Word on Time

Establishing time standards can be a long and tedious process. There can be many pitfalls when establishing them, and the following points should help in avoiding these pitfalls.

1. Recognize the need and purpose for the standards; then, determine the most appropriate and economical technique for establishing them.

2. When standards are used for productivity measures, improve operations first before setting time standards. This ensures that the times are based on efficient operations.

3. When used in incentive programs, avoid problems by having all parties involved agree to the method for establishing standards and the conditions underlying them.

4. Use a computer spreadsheet program to set up and maintain time standards.

5. Finally, establish a system for maintaining the time standards to keep them realistic and current.

Figure 2.11. Impact of Technology on Warehouse Time

The following chart illustrates time spent on shipping and receiving activities in a hypothetical distribution facility. It also shows the effect various systems can have on reducing activity time. This is important to note because time saved is money saved. "Regular (manual)" refers to no use of barcode, shipping error rates at 2% to 4%, and inventory accuracy at 75% by item, quantity, and location. "Improved" refers to use of barcode for all material handling activities, RF-linked terminals for real-time computer updates, shipping error rates less than 1%, and inventory accuracy at 99.9%. As the chart shows, improved processes result in a 30% to 50% increase in productivity, improved customer service, and reduced operating expenses. "Re-engineered" refers to use of electronic data interchange (EDI) or e-commerce to manage orders and no matching of packing slips or invoices. Items are received with advance shipping notices (ASNs), so receiving validates receipt and, 60% of the time, enables cross docking. Shipments automatically trigger invoices to customers.

Activity	Regular (Manual)	Improved	Re-engineered
Issue PO to supplier	3–20 min	3–20 min	Auto: EDI, e-commerce
Receive material	7–20 min	7–20 min	7–10 min
Verify receipt	15–45 min	7–15 min	Auto: ASN
Store material	8–20 min	4–10 min	4–10 min
Update inventory	300–900 min	2–5 min	Auto
Process supplier invoice	5–25 min	5–25 min	Auto
Receive customer PO	3–20 min	3–20 min	Auto
Pick for shipment	5–25 min	3–7 min	3–7 min
Update inventory	300–900 min	2–5 min	Auto
Issue customer invoice	3–15 min	3–15 min	Auto

Reprinted with permission from Rick Bushnell, Insightu.org, Surf City, NJ.

Common Warehouse Time Standards

This section is a compilation of common warehouse time standards that can be used for time study analysis of different warehouse operations. The first two tables are time standards involved in the operation of narrow aisle reach trucks. These standards were provided by Hyster, a long-time manufacturer of material handling trucks and equipment.

Figure 2.12. Operation: Retrieving and Putting Away a Pallet Using a 24-Volt Narrow Aisle Reach Truck

This element includes all the time necessary to retrieve and put away a pallet using a 24-volt narrow aisle reach truck. The element begins with travel from the point of origin to the retrieval/insertion location based on sample variables provided and using published speeds set by the truck manufacturer. It ends with travel back to the point of origin.

Sample Variables:
Rack Height: 22.7 ft
Aisle Length: 300 ft
Out-of-Aisle Travel: 50 ft

NL: Not Loaded
RL: Rated Load
L: Loaded

Retrieve Cycle	Speed/Time	Distance/ Frequency	Seconds[3]
Travel NL	7 mph	200 ft[1]	19.5
Lift NL	57 fpm	11.3 ft[2]	11.9
Lower RL	91 fpm	11.3 ft[2]	7.5
Extend NL	3.1 sec	1 time	3.1
Retract RL	3.6 sec	1 time	3.6
Tilt NL	2 sec	1 time	2.0
Sideshift NL	2 sec	1 time	2.0
Travel L	6.8 mph	200 ft[1]	20.1
		Cycle Total:	69.7

Put Cycle	Speed/Time	Distance/ Frequency	Seconds[3]
Travel L	6.8 mph	200 ft[1]	20.1
Lift RL	38 fpm	11.3 ft[2]	17.9
Lower NL	83 fpm	11.3 ft[2]	8.2
Retract NL	3.1 sec	1 time	3.1
Extend RL	3.6 sec	1 time	3.6
Tilt RL	2.5 sec	1 time	2.5
Sideshift RL	2.5 sec	1 time	2.5
Travel NL	7 mph	200 ft[1]	19.5
		Cycle Total:	77.4

Assumptions:

Speeds are based on Hyster Narrow Aisle Reach Truck Model N30XMR3.

For this element, the Rated Load and the Load are equal.

[1] Distance traveled is half the aisle length plus out-of-aisle travel. (1/2 x 300 ft) + 50 ft

[2] Lifting and lowering height is half the rack height. 1/2 x 22.7 ft

[3] These times do not include any information processing or personal fatigue and delay allowances. It includes the time involved for directly handling the lift truck.

Reprinted with permission from Hyster Company, Greenville, NC.

Figure 2.13. Operation: Retrieving and Putting Away a Pallet Using a 36-Volt Narrow Aisle Reach Truck

This element includes all the time necessary to retrieve and put away a pallet using a 36-volt narrow aisle reach truck. The element begins with travel from the point of origin to the retrieval/insertion location based on sample variables provided and using published speeds set by the truck manufacturer. It ends with travel back to the point of origin.

Sample Variables:
Rack Height: 27.7 ft
Aisle Length: 300 ft
Out-of-Aisle Travel: 50 ft

NL: Not Loaded
RL: Rated Load
L: Loaded

Retrieve Cycle	Speed/Time	Distance/ Frequency	Seconds[3]
Travel NL	7.7 mph	200 ft[1]	17.7
Lift NL	107 fpm	11.3 ft[2]	6.4
Lower RL	105 fpm	11.3 ft[2]	6.5
Extend NL	3.1 sec	1 time	3.1
Retract RL	3.6 sec	1 time	3.6
Tilt NL	2 sec	1 time	2.0
Sideshift NL	2 sec	1 time	2.0
Travel L	5.4 mph	200 ft[1]	25.3
		Cycle Total:	66.6

Put Cycle	Speed/Time	Distance/ Frequency	Seconds[3]
Travel L	5.4 mph	200 ft[1]	25.3
Lift RL	67 fpm	11.3 ft[2]	10.1
Lower NL	90 fpm	11.3 ft[2]	7.6
Retract NL	3.1 sec	1 time	3.1
Extend RL	3.6 sec	1 time	3.6
Tilt RL	2.5 sec	1 time	2.5
Sideshift RL	2.5 sec	1 time	2.5
Travel NL	7.7 mph	200 ft[1]	17.7
		Cycle Total:	72.4

Assumptions:

Speeds are based on Hyster Narrow Aisle Reach Truck Model N45XMXR3.

For this element, the Rated Load and the Load are equal.

[1] Distance traveled is half the aisle length plus out-of-aisle travel. (1/2 x 300 ft) + 50 ft

[2] Lifting and lowering height is half the rack height. 1/2 x 22.7 ft

[3] These times do not include any information processing or personal fatigue, and delay allowances. It includes the time involved for directly handling the lift truck.

Reprinted with permission from Hyster Company, Greenville, NC.

The remaining tables are time standards derived from the *Standardization of Work Measurement: Defense Work Measurement Standard Time Data Program, DoD 5010.15.1-M*, last updated January 1977. (Note: There have been no known revisions to this Department of Defense document since 1977. Although quite dated, the standards that address manual operations are still relevant for a number of material handling analyses.)

Figure 2.14. Operation: Document Processing — Per Line Item Received

This element includes all the time necessary to perform document processing incident to the receipt of one line item of material. The element begins with a move of the receipt document preparatory to matching against the material; includes the time to verify the stock number, item description, and unit of issue; and ends when the checker annotates the document with the quantity received, the total number of containers and pallets received, and the stock location of the material.

Element	Minutes
Scan sheet for reference points	0.036
Verify:	
Stock number	0.091
Item description	0.031
Unit of issue	0.040
Obtain and replace pencil in pocket	0.064
Annotate:	
Quantity received	0.049
Total number of containers	0.090
Storage location	0.120
Tally:	
Count tally (tick) marks	0.031
Make calculation	0.022
Write total pallets	0.107
Total normal time	0.681

Figure 2.15. Operation: Document Processing — Checking Per Line Item Packed

This element includes all the time necessary to perform document processing incident to the packing of one line item of material. The element begins with a reach to the material documents in immediate packing area; includes time for the packer to verify the material as being correct as to stock number, item, and unit of issue; and ends when the document is put aside.

Element	Minutes
Obtain document	0.025
Scan sheet for reference points	0.036
Verify:	
Stock number	0.091
Item description	0.031
Unit of issue	0.040
Put aside document	0.022
Total normal time	0.245

Figure 2.16. Operation: Document Processing — Per Pallet Received or Shipped

This element includes all the time necessary to perform document processing incident to the receipt or shipment of one pallet of material. The element begins with a visual count of the number of containers on the pallet, includes the time to record the total number of containers on the pallet, and ends when a tally (tick) mark has been made to record the pallet.

Element	Minutes
Count pieces	0.055
Obtain and put aside document	0.047
Obtain and replace pencil in pocket	0.064
Post total pieces	0.020
Obtain and put aside worksheet	0.047
Make tally (tick) mark	0.010
Total normal time	0.243

Figure 2.17. Operation: Obtain and Operate Manual Pallet Jack

This element includes all the time to secure, start, stop, and return pallet jack. The element begins with securing the pallet jack; includes start, stop, run in, empty, raise forks, run out loaded, position to drop, drop the forks; and ends with run out empty.

Element	Minutes
Get pallet jack	0.030
Start pallet jack	0.019
Stop pallet jack	0.035
Run in empty	0.071
Raise forks	0.248
Run out loaded	0.155
Start pallet jack – loaded	0.019
Stop pallet jack – loaded	0.035
Position to drop	0.128
Drop forks (knob control)	0.061
Run out empty	0.108
Total normal time:	0.909

Figure 2.18. Operation: Turn Container (Slide)

This element includes all the time necessary to turn a container by sliding on a table, conveyor, etc. The element begins with a reach to grasp the container and ends with the return of hands after turning the boxes.

Element	Minutes	
	90 Degrees	180 Degrees
Small container (8" x 8" x 8")	0.014	0.017
Medium container (12" x 12" x 12")	0.029	0.058
Large container (24" x 24" x 24")	0.040	0.079

Figure 2.19. Operation: Travel Times for Manual Pallet Jack

This element includes the times necessary to complete a round-trip of travel. The travel time includes a start, stop, and normal turns, and it provides for one-way travel empty and one-way loaded. Time also is included to get pallet jack, run in empty, raise forks, run out loaded, position pallet to drop, and to drop pallet. Times are for a round-trip based on one-way distance.

Distance (Feet)	Constant Time (Minutes)	Travel Time Empty (Minutes)	Travel Time Loaded (Minutes)	Total Round Trip Time (Minutes)
10	0.909	0.061	0.092	1.062
20	0.909	0.112	0.163	1.184
30	0.909	0.163	0.235	1.307
40	0.909	0.214	0.306	1.429
50	0.909	0.265	0.377	1.551
60	0.909	0.316	0.449	1.674
70	0.909	0.367	0.520	1.796
80	0.909	0.418	0.592	1.919
90	0.909	0.469	0.663	2.041
100	0.909	0.520	0.734	2.163

Each additional 10 feet one-way distance: 0.122 Minutes

Distance (Feet)	Loaded		Empty	
	Paces To Move	Time (Minutes)	Paces To Move	Time (Minutes)
10	9	0.092	6	0.061
20	16	0.163	11	0.112
30	23	0.235	16	0.163
40	30	0.306	21	0.214
50	37	0.377	26	0.265
60	44	0.449	31	0.316
70	51	0.520	36	0.367
80	58	0.592	41	0.418
90	65	0.663	46	0.469
100	72	0.734	51	0.520

Figure 2.20. Operation: Package Handling — Mixed Loads

This element includes time to gain control of a package; slide the package from a stack; orient to identify the package as required; move the package to a pallet, skid, or cart; and return to the stack for the next package. This element includes removing packages from stacks up to 72 inches high and placing packages on pallets, skids, or carts up to a level of 42 inches.

These time values also apply to the operation of moving packages from a pallet, skid, or cart to a stack. The same limitation as to maximum stack height and maximum pallet, skid, or cart height applies to this operation.

These time values include time only for the manual operation of handling and identifying the packages and apply when a variety of commodities are being handled.

Typical operations covered by these time values would include unloading and loading freight cars or trailers when a variety of items are being handled.

Package/Density Pounds Per Cubic Foot	Weight–Pounds Up To and Including							
	5	15	25	35	45	55	65	75
	Normal Time in Minutes Per Package							
1	0.082	0.157	0.187	0.213	0.236	0.256	—	—
2	0.073	0.139	0.167	0.191	0.212	0.232	0.251	0.268
3	0.047	0.083	0.158	0.181	0.200	0.218	0.237	0.254
5	0.044	0.077	0.147	0.168	0.187	0.205	0.223	0.239
10	0.040	0.070	0.134	0.154	0.172	0.189	0.205	0.222
15	0.038	0.067	0.127	0.146	0.164	0.181	0.197	0.212
20	0.037	0.064	0.123	0.142	0.159	0.175	0.191	0.206
30	0.035	0.062	0.118	0.136	0.152	0.169	0.184	0.199
50	0.033	0.058	0.110	0.129	0.146	0.161	0.176	0.190
70	0.032	0.056	0.107	0.124	0.141	0.156	0.171	0.185

Determine time as follows:

1. Locate the corresponding weight, on the top of the table, for the average weight per piece handled.
2. Locate the corresponding density, on the left side of the table, to the average density per piece handled.
3. Read across from the density to the weight column and extract the time per piece handled.

Note: Workers required to handle container.

One worker – Average weight per container up to and including 75 lbs. for 1 man, or 1 x time value from above table.

Two workers – Average weight per container 76 lbs. to 150 lbs.

    (a) Divide the average weight by 2; this is the average weight handled by each worker.

    (b) Select time value from table.

    (c) Multiply the time value by 2 for the two workers required to handle the material.

Figure 2.21. Operation: Package Handling — Solid Loads

This element includes time to gain control of a package; slide the package from a stack; move the package to a pallet, skid, or cart; and return to the stack for the next package. This element includes removing packages from stacks up to a level of 72 inches high and placing packages on pallets, skids, or carts up to a level of 42 inches.

These time values also apply to the operation of moving packages from a pallet, skid, or cart to a stack. The same limitation as to maximum stack height and maximum pallet, skid, or cart height applies to this operation.

These time values include time only for the manual operation of handling packages. Typical operations covered by these time values are: unloading and loading freight cars or trailers when only one commodity is being handled.

Package/Density Pounds Per Cubic Foot	Weight–Pounds Up To and Including							
	5	15	25	35	45	55	65	75
	Normal Time in Minutes Per Package							
1	0.073	0.145	0.175	0.199	0.220	0.239	—	—
2	0.065	0.130	0.157	0.178	0.199	0.217	0.235	0.251
3	0.041	0.074	0.148	0.169	0.187	0.205	0.222	0.238
5	0.038	0.068	0.137	0.157	0.175	0.192	0.209	0.224
10	0.034	0.062	0.125	0.143	0.161	0.177	0.193	0.208
15	0.032	0.059	0.118	0.137	0.154	0.170	0.185	0.200
20	0.031	0.058	0.115	0.132	0.149	0.164	0.179	0.194
30	0.030	0.055	0.110	0.127	0.143	0.158	0.173	0.187
50	0.028	0.052	0.103	0.121	0.137	0.151	0.165	0.179
70	0.027	0.050	0.100	0.116	0.132	0.146	0.161	0.174

Determine time as follows:

1. Locate the corresponding weight, on the top of the table, for the average weight per piece handled.
2. Locate the corresponding density, on the left side of the table, to the average density per piece handled.
3. Read across from the density to the weight column and extract the time per piece handled.

Note: Workers required to handle container.

One worker – Average weight per container up to and including 75 lbs. for 1 man, or 1 x time value from above table.

Two workers – Average weight per container 76 lbs. to 150 lbs.

   (a)   Divide the average weight by 2; this is the average weight handled by each worker.

   (b)   Select time value from table.

   (3)   Multiply the time value by 2 for the two workers required to handle the material.

Figure 2.22. Operation: Non-Powered Equipment and Pedestrian Travel Times

Travel times for manual pallet jack. This element includes the time necessary to complete a one-way trip of travel. The travel times include a start and stop and normal turns. No times are included for run in, pick up, run out, position, or drop load. The time for moving a loaded manual pallet jack can also be used as the time for pushing a *loaded* two- or four-wheeled cart.

Travel times for walking unobstructed. This element includes all the time necessary to walk from one working area to another. The element begins with a turning of the body toward the direction to be walked (up to 90 degree turn) and ends with a stop in front of the destination. The times noted are for one-way travel and a 27-inch walking pace.

Travel times for walking obstructed. This element includes all the time necessary to carry or push an object from one working area to another. The element begins with a turning of the body toward the direction to be walked (up to 90 degree turn) and ends with a stop in front of the destination. The times noted are for one-way travel and a 27-inch walking pace. The time for walking obstructed can also be used as the time for pushing an *empty* two- or four-wheeled cart.

One-Way Travel Distance (Feet)	Travel Time (Minutes)		Walk Unobstructed (27-Inch Pace)	Walk Obstructed (27-Inch Pace)
	Manual Pallet Jack			
	Empty	Loaded		
20	0.112	0.163	0.102	0.113
40	0.214	0.306	0.183	0.204
60	0.316	0.449	0.263	0.295
80	0.418	0.592	0.343	0.385
100	0.520	0.734	0.422	0.475
120	0.622	0.877	0.502	0.566
140	0.724	1.020	0.582	0.657
160	0.826	1.163	0.662	0.748
180	0.928	1.306	0.742	0.838
200	1.030	1.448	0.822	0.929
220	1.132	1.591	0.903	1.020
240	1.234	1.734	0.983	1.111
260	1.336	1.877	1.063	1.201
280	1.438	2.020	1.142	1.291
300	1.540	2.162	1.222	1.382
320	1.642	2.305	1.302	1.473
340	1.744	2.448	1.382	1.564
360	1.846	2.591	1.462	1.654
380	1.948	2.734	1.542	1.745
400	2.050	2.876	1.623	1.836
Each Additional 100 Feet	0.510	0.714	0.400	0.454
Maximum Speed (Feet/Minute)	196	140	250	221

Figure 2.23. Operation: Lift Truck, Travel Into and Out of Trailer

This element starts with the movement of the lift truck either: (1) prior to entering carrier, or (2) toward the carrier door. The element includes all the time necessary to move into or out of trailers with the use of a lift truck. The element ends when the lift truck stops in front of the material or pallet.

Element	Minutes	
	Loaded	No Load
Out of trailer	0.233	0.226
Into trailer	0.216	0.200
Into trailer and drop pallet	0.241	—
Into trailer and pick up pallet	—	0.226

Figure 2.24. Operation: Lift Truck (6000 Pounds)

This element starts with lift operator on lift truck, includes time values for all basic motions that are performed by a standard rider-type lift truck with capacities up to three thousand pounds, and ends with lift operator on truck.

Element	Minutes			
	No Load	1000 Pounds	2000 Pounds	3000 Pounds
Forward	0.002	0.002	0.002	0.002
Reverse	0.002	0.002	0.002	0.002
Accelerate	0.030	0.025	0.025	0.025
Stop	0.020	0.033	0.034	0.035
Run in 1st level	0.080	0.080	0.080	0.070
Run in 2nd level	0.080	0.090	0.110	0.100
Run in 3rd level	0.080	0.120	0.130	0.120
Run out 1st level	0.060	0.065	0.065	0.060
Run out 2nd level	0.060	0.065	0.070	0.060
Run out 3rd level	0.060	0.070	0.070	0.080
Right forward	0.055	0.055	0.055	0.055
Right reverse	0.055	0.055	0.055	0.055
Right forward stop	0.070	0.070	0.070	0.075
Right reverse stop	0.065	0.085	0.080	0.080
Left forward	0.055	0.055	0.055	0.055
Left reverse	0.055	0.055	0.055	0.055
Left forward stop	0.060	0.060	0.060	0.060
Left reverse stop	0.065	0.075	0.075	0.065
Tilt	0.025	0.025	0.025	0.025
Lift up	0.003	0.003	0.003	0.003
Drop down	0.003	0.005	0.005	0.005

Figure 2.25. Operation: Lift Truck (4000 Pounds, Electric), Travel with Pallet

This element starts with start of fork movement or start of machine travel. This element includes all the time necessary for the forks to move up or down the desired distance or for the lift truck to travel the desired distance. It ends after completion of desired movement.

	Minutes		
Element	No Load	2000 Pounds	4000 Pounds
Fork movement per 6 inches			
Up	0.014	0.019	0.026
Down	0.014	0.014	0.015
Start run – first 10 feet	0.036	0.036	0.036
Run each additional foot			
Fast	0.003	0.003	0.003
Slow	—	0.005	0.005

Figure 2.26. Operation: Lift Truck (6000 Pounds, Electric), Travel with Pallet

This element starts with start of fork movement or start of machine travel. This element includes all the time necessary for the forks to move up or down the desired distance or for the lift truck to travel the desired distance. It ends after completion of desired movement.

	Minutes		
Element	No Load	2000 Pounds	4000 Pounds
Fork movement per 6 inches			
Up	0.020	0.025	0.028
Down	0.018	0.017	0.017
Start run – first 10 feet	0.054	0.060	0.060
Run each additional foot			
Fast	0.003	0.003	0.003
Slow	—	—	0.005

Figure 2.27. Operation: Operate Lift Truck 1 (Electric)

Starts with actuating controls, includes all the time to actuate controls and perform the desired move, and ends after completion of move.

Element	Minutes
Run in from two feet	0.062
Run out to two feet	0.038
Actuate controls – start (forward or reverse)	0.023
Fork operation (controls start and stop)	0.026
Tilt mast	0.053

Figure 2.28. Operation: Operate Lift Truck 2 (Electric)

Starts with reach to actuate controls; includes the time to grasp and move controls, and to start and stop the desired movements of the forks; and ends with release of controls after movement stops.

Element	Minutes
Raise forks – first foot	0.052
Raise forks – each additional foot	0.037
Lower forks – first foot	0.038
Lower forks – each additional foot	0.023
Tilt back mast – first 10 degrees	0.035
Tilt back mast – additional 10 degrees	0.020

Figure 2.29. Operation: Pallet, Load Into and Out of Trailer With Lift Truck

This element starts with a pallet on lift truck at entrance to trailer; includes all the time necessary to move pallet into trailer, drop it, and travel out; and ends with lift truck returning to starting point. It includes the time to pick up pallet and travel out of trailer.

Element	Minutes
Move pallet into truck trailer and return	0.467
Move pallet out of trailer	0.459

Figure 2.30. Operation: Material, Pick Up, Transport, Drop With Lift Truck

Starts with lift truck operator walking to lift truck; includes the movements necessary to get on lift truck, travel to pickup point, pick up material on skid or pallet, travel to drop point, set down material, and back clear; and ends with lift truck clearing skid or pallet and ready to travel.

Element	Minutes
Mount lift truck	0.137
Dismount lift truck	0.130
Start lift truck engine	0.091
Shift lift truck into gear	0.065
Release hand brake	0.037
Set hand brake	0.037
Shut off lift truck engine	0.020
Mount, dismount, start, stop, and release handbrake, shift into gear	0.517

Figure 2.31. Operation: Unit Load Handling Times

Starts with lift truck operator walking to lift truck; includes the movements necessary to get on lift truck, travel to pickup point, pick up material on skid or pallet, travel to drop point, set down material, and back clear; and ends with lift truck clearing skid or pallet and ready to travel.

Element	Time for Single Pallet Handling (Minutes)					
	Lift Truck		Electric Pallet Jack[1]		Manual Pallet Jack[2]	
	Pick Up[3]	Stack[4]	Pick Up	Stack	Pick Up	Stack
Pallet on floor, no turn required to pick up, stock, or travel	0.170	0.165	0.213	0.206	0.255	0.248
Pallet on floor, turn and stop prior to pick up, stack, or travel	0.245	0.235	0.306	0.294	0.368	0.353
Pallet in storage:						
First level[5]	0.315	0.300	0.394	0.375	0.473	0.450
First or second level	0.353	0.379	0.441	0.474		
Second level only[6]	0.392	0.457	0.490	0.571		
Up to three levels	0.452	0.509				
Up to four levels	0.502	0.574				
Third level only	0.649	0.770				

[1] Derived from lift truck time. Also applies to walkie lift trucks.

[2] Derived from lift truck time.

[3] Operation: Pick up pallets — lift truck. This element includes all the time necessary to pick up a pallet of material. The element begins with a turn of the lift truck (if applicable) to run the forks into the pallet, includes the time to move the pallet off and/or away from other palletized material, and ends with the forks lowered to 4 inches above floor level and the lift truck prepared to travel with the load.

[4] Operation: Stack pallets — lift truck. This element includes all the time necessary to stack a pallet using a lift truck. The element begins with a turn of the lift truck into the stow area, includes the time to raise the pallet and to place the pallet on a stack or the floor, and ends with the forks removed from the pallet and raised or lowered to 4 inches above floor level and the truck prepared to travel away from the stack of material.

[5] May be used for lower tier racks (on floor or on rack member).

[6] Applies to transport carts.

Figure 2.32. Operation: Loading and Unloading Times

Starts with lift truck operator walking to lift truck; includes the movements necessary to get on lift truck, travel to pickup point, pick up material on skid or pallet, travel to drop point, set down material, and back clear; and ends with lift truck clearing skid or pallet and ready to travel.

Element	Time Per Pallet in Carrier (Minutes)[1]					
	Trailer			Railcar		
	Lift Truck	Electric Pallet Jack[2]	Manual Pallet Jack	Lift Truck	Electric Pallet Jack[2]	Manual Pallet Jack
Palletized loads	0.678	0.848	1.017	0.771	0.964	1.157
Add for second-level pallet[3]	0.077	0.096		0.077	0.096	
Floor loads[4]	0.603	0.754	0.905	0.696	0.870	1.044
Loading						
Palletized loads	0.677	0.846	1.016	0.769	0.961	1.154
Add for second-level pallet[3]	0.157	0.196		0.157	0.196	
Floor loads[4]	0.607	0.759	0.911	0.699	0.874	1.049

[1] These elements include all of the time necessary for travel and pallet handling in the carrier. The elements begin with the movement of the transport vehicle at the carrier door prior to entering the carrier. The elements end with the transport vehicle on the dock immediately outside the carrier door.

These elements do not include individual case handling in the carrier or any travel or handling time on the dock.

The travel times are derived from Operation: Travel Into/Out of Boxcar/Trailer. The handling times are derived from Figure 2.32, Unit Load Handling Times.

[2] These times apply to walkie lift trucks.

[3] If pallets are stacked two high in the carrier, these times must be added for all pallets on the second level.

[4] This element assumes that material is floor loaded in the carrier and it will be manually palletized before pallet unloading or manually stacked on the floor after pallet loading. No time is included for individual case handling.

Figure 2.33. Operation: Assemble Carton

This element starts with a decision to select a proper-sized carton. It includes all the time necessary to select, assemble, seal the bottom, and invert a carton to a ready-to-pack position. It ends with the release of the carton in position.

Element	Time to Assemble (Minutes)		
	Small Carton (8" x 8" x 8")	Medium Carton (12" x 12" x 12")	Large Carton (24" x 24" x 24")
In tote tray	0.277	0.300	0.359
Overhead	0.310	0.333	0.392
Adjacent – to five feet	0.334	0.357	0.416
Behind – to five feet	0.356	0.379	0.439

Figure 2.34. Operation: Push Cart (Loaded)

This element starts with a step to the end of the cart. It includes all the time necessary to release cart brake, grasp handle, push a loaded cart, stop cart, and return to starting point. It ends with the release of the cart and return to starting point.

Total Weight Pushed (lbs)	Minutes Per Distance Travelled					
	5 Steps	10 Steps	20 Steps	30 Steps	40 Steps	50 Steps
10	0.203	0.311	0.527	0.743	0.959	1.175
20	0.205	0.313	0.529	0.745	0.961	1.177
30	0.208	0.316	0.532	0.748	0.964	1.180
40	0.209	0.317	0.533	0.749	0.965	1.181
50	0.211	0.319	0.535	0.751	0.967	1.183
60	0.212	0.320	0.536	0.752	0.968	1.184
70	0.215	0.323	0.539	0.755	0.971	1.187
80	0.216	0.324	0.540	0.756	0.972	1.188
90	0.218	0.326	0.542	0.758	0.974	1.190
100	0.220	0.328	0.544	0.760	0.976	1.192
200	0.238	0.346	0.562	0.778	0.994	1.216

Figure 2.35. Miscellaneous Material Handling Standards

Operation	Minutes
1. Apply 9-1/2" x 8" label to surface	0.121

2. Tape document to container
    For first piece of tape
    For each additional piece of tape
	
	0.160
	0.127

3. Obtain empty container (up to 5 lbs), put aside full (up to 35 lbs) onto conveyor	0.116

4. Open sealed container
   Easy to open, one tape on container
     Small carton (8" x 8" x 8")
     Medium carton (12" x 12" x 12")
     Large carton (24" x 24" x 24")
 	
   Difficult to open, excessive tape, and/or flaps glued
     Small carton (8" x 8" x 8")
     Medium carton (12" x 12" x 12")
     Large carton (24" x 24" x 24")
	
	0.209
	0.231
	0.263
	
	0.238
	0.271
	0.405

5. Push pallet on conveyor (includes bend, grasp, start pallet in motion, and push pallet four paces)	0.099

6. Count line items on a sheet (includes obtain and put aside a sheet and count the number of line items on the sheet)
   Get and put aside sheet – reach 18"
   Time per line item on sheet
	
	0.045
	0.010

7. Place plastic tray on conveyor line (includes pick up and placement of 8-lb, 24" x 32" tray on conveyor)	0.079

Chapter 3
WAREHOUSE SPACE CALCULATIONS

Determining the amount of space required to run an efficient and effective warehouse requires a combination of mathematics, experience, creativity, and common sense. It begins with a thorough understanding of the warehouse's primary mission or purpose. Will this be a facility whose primary goal is to *store* inventory, or will this be a facility that *moves* products? The first purpose puts emphasis on calculating storage space and maximizing the utilization of that space, while the second focuses on optimizing throughput and maintaining an unimpeded flow of product in and out of a facility.

Figures 3.1 and **3.2** illustrate these two extremes. **Figure 3.1** is an example of a cross dock facility where product moves in and out of the building with little or no storage. Cross docking, just-in-time systems, and flow-through warehousing are growing trends, arising from pressure to reduce cycle times and increase inventory turns. With these systems, more active warehouse space is needed, thus requiring the careful planning of the *receiving, shipping, and order processing space*. On the other hand, many operations need to store inventory, and their warehouses must be designed around efficient storage and access to inventory. **Figure 3.2** is a typical facility for traditional warehousing, where calculations for *storage space* dominate the design process.

Most warehouses are somewhere in between — geared toward both optimizing space *and* increasing throughput, while maximizing the use of available resources, such as labor and equipment. All these must be accomplished while keeping products constantly protected from damage, theft, weather, and fire, and keeping employees safe from accidents and injuries. The key to satisfying these conflicting goals lies in a systematic facility design process that includes calculating space requirements and adopting space guidelines.

Figure 3.3 outlines the basic approach to the warehouse design process, which is divided into four main parts:

1. The first step is to *develop the design criteria*. This includes:

• Auditing the operations in order to document the existing processes, to provide a benchmark for alternative designs, and to identify and document customer requirements.

• Gathering relevant, accurate, and reliable information. This may be difficult, as most organizations do not keep accurate records. They may also not be in a format that is readily useful. Thus, a substantial amount of design time is spent on interpreting and understanding the data.

• Analyzing and managing the collected data. Here, forecasts and other business plans are identified and incorporated to complete the design criteria.

2. With the design criteria in place, you can begin to *develop design alternatives* by using a combination of spreadsheet and layout tools. This is composed of two major steps:

• Developing alternative designs based on the design criteria.

• Calculating the space, equipment, labor, and cost requirements for each design.

3. Next, *evaluate alternatives* both quantitatively and qualitatively. Capital and operating costs, ease of implementation, and design flexibility are just some of the basic criteria used to evaluate the alternatives.

4. *Select and implement* the final system.

Steps 3 and 4 will be described in greater detail in the next chapter. In this chapter, the discussion will concentrate on using space calculations, standards, and guidelines to carry out Steps 1 and 2 — *developing the design criteria* and *generating design alternatives* for evaluation. Focus will be on the main operating areas of the

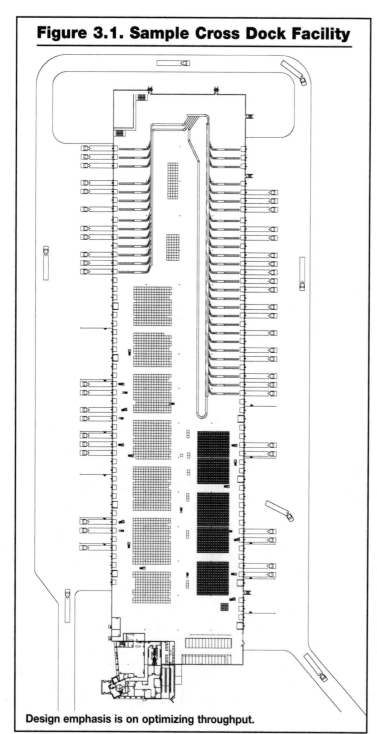

Figure 3.1. Sample Cross Dock Facility

Design emphasis is on optimizing throughput.

Figure 3.2. Sample Storage Facility

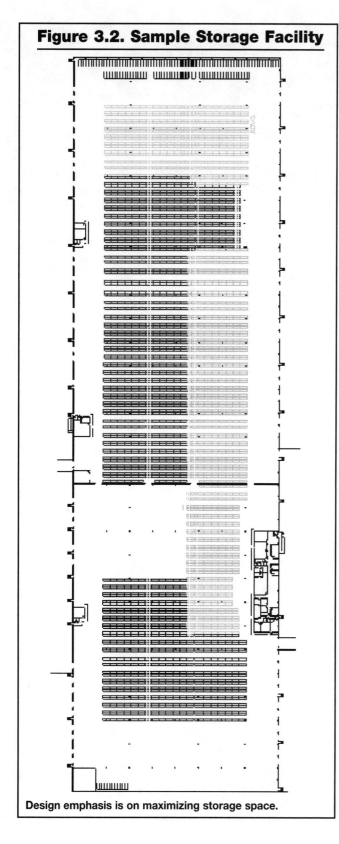

Design emphasis is on maximizing storage space.

warehouse — receiving and shipping docks, storage areas, and order processing areas. For this process, it is assumed that management has already made the strategic decision on whether design changes are to be made to an existing building or whether a new facility is to be built. In either scenario, the above design approach still applies.

There are many possible combinations of products, equipment, and operating systems. In this section, some basic strategies are provided to help you determine the best possible combination of products, equipment, and operating systems. Tables and charts are included that should be integral components of your library of decision-making tools.

Receiving and Shipping Docks

A substantial part of warehouse operations is concentrated in the receiving and shipping areas, or the dock areas. Cross docking and just-in-time principles have made it imperative that the docks be designed properly. Docks today have to accept more frequent deliveries and make more shipments from a wide assortment of tractor-trailers and delivery vehicles. Failure to plan carefully for the facility's shipping and receiving needs may result in inadequately sized areas, costly future renovations, and equipment problems. Poor planning and design may cost demurrage for delaying carriers, impede efficient shipping and receiving operations, result in product and facility damages, and lead to personnel injuries.

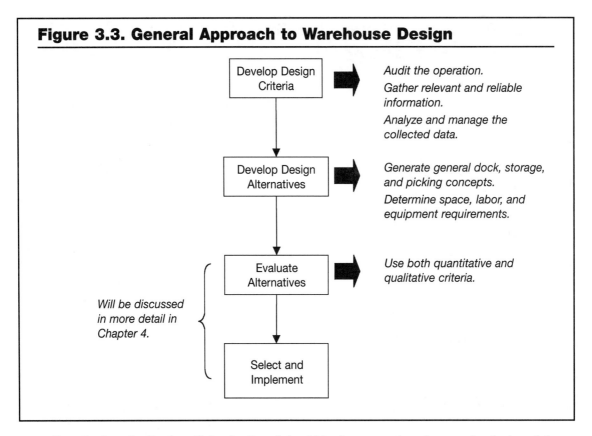

Figure 3.3. General Approach to Warehouse Design

Develop Design Criteria ➡ Audit the operation.
Gather relevant and reliable information.
Analyze and manage the collected data.

Develop Design Alternatives ➡ Generate general dock, storage, and picking concepts.
Determine space, labor, and equipment requirements.

Evaluate Alternatives ➡ Use both quantitative and qualitative criteria.

Will be discussed in more detail in Chapter 4.

Select and Implement

Developing the Design Criteria. Receiving/shipping operations have to be designed for the average and peak load estimates of the design year. The design year may be 5 to 7 years into the future. Design year estimates are often calculated by using historical data. Design year requirements are expressed in terms of expected:

1. Frequency of receipts and shipments by truck or by rail

2. Number and description of tractor-trailers, vans, and delivery vehicles arriving

3. Dimensions of tractor-trailers, vans, and delivery vehicles arriving

4. Arrival times

5. Loading and unloading times

6. Volume by product lines

7. Volume by mode of transportation.

Some questions to be answered include:

1. What different processes are to be carried out on the dock?

2. How do these processes interact and affect each other and the rest of the warehouse?

3. What is the number and location of carriers who will deliver to the facility?

4. Which carriers will deliver/pick up?

5. What other modes of transportation will be used?

6. What is the volume in cubic feet and what are the typical shipment sizes in cubic feet for each carrier/receiver?

7. Are loads unitized or hand stacked?

8. Are unitized loads on slipsheets, on pallets, or on other mediums?

Developing Design Alternatives. The design of the dock area includes the following steps:

1. Determining the location of the docks

2. Determining the number and size of dock doors required

3. Determining the size and layout of the staging area

4. Specifying other dock equipment needs

5. Allowing space on the dock for other functions.

Step 1. Determining the Proper Location of the Docks. Depending on the layout of the facility, the receiving and shipping dock doors can be in the same area as in a U-shaped product flow or in different areas of the warehouse, as in an L-shaped or I-shaped product flow. **Figure 3.4** illustrates these alternative flow patterns. Having the shipping and receiving doors close to each other allows for more flexibility for dock usage, promotes faster cross docking capability, and permits consolidation of the supervisory function for the two operations. In addition, less overall space may be required. Conversely, separating them may improve security and reduce congestion.

In some cases, space restrictions may be the overriding factor in deciding where to locate docks. However, when there are a number of choices possible,

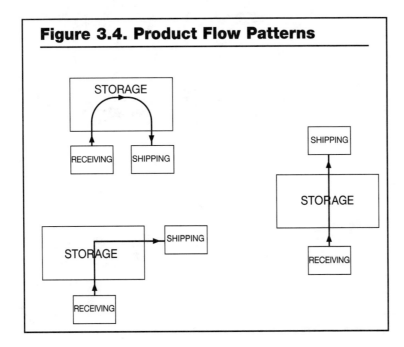

Figure 3.4. Product Flow Patterns

there are other practical factors that should be considered.

• It is safest and quickest for tractor-trailers and over-the-road vehicles to approach the docks in a counterclockwise direction. In this direction, the driver can look out the driver's side window when backing up. The distance between centers of the doors should be at least 13 feet. The actual distance between the doors may be greater, depending upon other factors such as building column spacing and staging requirements. The greater the distance between doors, the less maneuvering is required by the tractor-trailer drivers.

• There must be sufficient apron space and a waiting area for trucks waiting to back in. For 13-foot door centers where trucks approach in a counterclockwise direction, the apron space should be approximately twice the length of the longest vehicle plus an additional 5 feet as a safety margin. As the distance between the doors increases, apron space can be reduced. For two-directional traffic, roads should be at least 26 feet wide.[1]

For one-way roads, the minimum width should be 13 feet. Gates and approaches to roadways should be at least 30 feet wide for two-directional traffic and at least 20 feet wide for one-way traffic. Wide-angle mirrors at blind corners, posted speed limits, no parking in areas of poor vision, separate pedestrian and vehicle traffic, and separate roadways for employees should keep accidents to a minimum.[2]

• Some facilities incorporate a landing strip into the driveway that is long enough to accommodate the longest trailer. **Figure 3.5** illustrates how the length of trailers has increased from

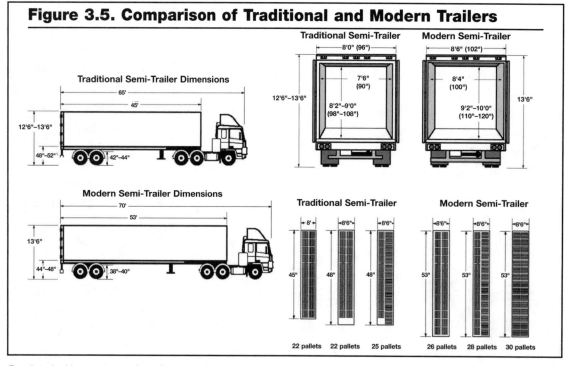

Figure 3.5. Comparison of Traditional and Modern Trailers

Reprinted with permission from Rite-Hite Corporation, Milwaukee, WI.

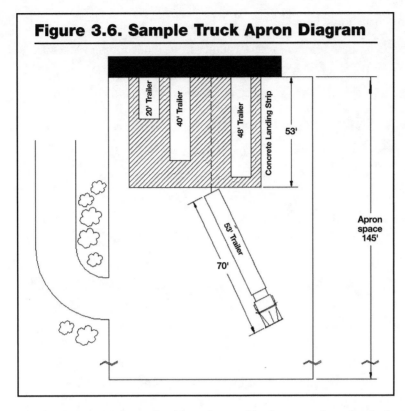

Figure 3.6. Sample Truck Apron Diagram

20' Trailer

40' Trailer

48' Trailer

Concrete Landing Strip

53'

53' Trailer

70'

Apron space 145'

48 feet to 53 feet. (Some states are even allowing 57-foot trailers.)[3] The landing strip should be made of concrete to prevent the landing gear and kingpin jack from sinking as they would in asphalt. **Figure 3.6** illustrates a sample dock layout with counter-clockwise vehicle approach and relative sizes for the landing strip and apron areas.

• Knowing the geography and climate of the area where you plan to locate the facility can also be valuable. In a hilly area, the docks may require special equipment. It is preferable to have a level approach to the docks, but if a slope is unavoidable, bumpers, seals, and canopies will need to be incorporated into the design to accommodate the angle of the truck's approach. If possible, the doors should face away from the prevailing winds. An important related consideration is the nature of the neighboring businesses. For example, if there are incinerators or large areas of garbage disposal nearby, locating the doors on the opposite side of your building should be considered to prevent smoke, fumes, flies, or other undesirable objects from entering the facility. In cold climates in the northern hemisphere, docks facing south will experience less heat loss than docks facing north.[4]

Step 2. Determining the Number and Size of Dock Doors Required. Insufficient and inadequately sized dock doors can substantially raise the cost of warehousing. If carriers have to sit in the yard because of insufficient doors, the carrier company may charge demurrage for waiting time. Door size is also critical. Dock doors that are too small will block access to a portion of the load, while larger doors will leave gaps, allowing heat to escape.

Number of Dock Doors. Knowledge of the operation's dock requirements is essential to determine the number of doors required. It is important to know the following design year requirements for typical and peak days:

• The pattern of truck arrivals and departures

• The time it takes to load or unload the trucks

• The total number of unit loads to be handled

• Description of loading and unloading operations (whether floor loaded, pallet loaded, hand stacked, etc.)

• The types and sizes of inbound and outbound vehicles

• The number of shifts of dock workers and drivers

• The configuration of the area required to stage, store, or process material.

If XYZ Company expects up to 20 carriers per 8-hour day and each carrier spends an average of 3 hours and 30 minutes at the facility, a door can only be used twice a day. Therefore, a minimum of 10 doors would be required. The number of operating shifts will also affect the number of doors. In our example, if the company operates on a two-shift schedule, only five doors will be required.

The above example illustrates a simple method for calculating dock door requirements, but unfortunately it is not realistic. Arrivals and departures differ and are sometimes concentrated in the middle of the morning and in the middle of the afternoon. There is a variety of carriers. Depending on the vehicle type and the type of loads, unloading/loading times can take a few minutes or many hours. Simulating dock operations may be necessary. Simulation involves duplicating the dock operation as a mathematical model. Inbound and outbound vehicles' arrival and departure times during peak periods are recorded and a statistical distribution identified. This distribution, with loading and unloading times for each specific carrier, simulate the traffic of vehicles dropping off and picking up material. First, a model is built for the existing operation to verify its validity and to use as a benchmark for testing scenarios. For example, an existing facility may currently operate with four dock doors. The model is run with four doors. Then the resulting statistics are verified against reality. If valid, a door is added, or subtracted, one at a time until a desired result is achieved or until the building layout prevents the addition of more doors. Management may expect a specific utilization rate, a minimum carrier waiting time, or a minimum average time that a carrier can stay at a warehouse — all statistics that can be collected in any simulation program.[5]

If simulation is not an option, dock equipment manufacturers can provide advice on the number of dock doors required. The installation of knock-out panels for future doors and knock-out pits for future dock levelers allow for flexibility and possible expansion.

Door Width. Data on the sizes of the tractor-trailers and other carrier vehicles has to be collected. In the past, most trailers were 96 inches, but current trailers have become wider — up to 102 inches. (Refer to **Figure 3.5**.) Loading and unloading the rearmost pallets in a 102-inch wide trailer can be difficult when the trailer is backed into a standard 96-inch wide dock door. Dock doors must be wide enough to accommodate both trailer sizes. Using 108-inch wide doors is recommended, as this allows a 102-inch wide trailer to back up to the dock with some margin for error.

Figure 3.7. Sample Dock Leveler

Reprinted with permission from Rite-Hite Corporation, Milwaukee, WI.

Figure 3.8. Sample Truck Leveler

Reprinted with permission from Rite-Hite Corporation, Milwaukee, WI.

Door Height. Maximum allowable height on interstate highways is 13 feet 6 inches, although some states allow higher vehicles on local roads. With standard 48-inch high docks, doors must be at least 10 feet high to allow full access to the trailer. Although most trailer beds are between 48 and 52 inches from the ground, new low-profile truck tires have made possible trailers — designed to fit larger loads — that sit only 30 to 36 inches off the ground. There are two methods for allowing warehouse vehicles to enter a truck lower than the dock.

• Dock Levelers (**Figure 3.7**). The most common approach is to bring the dock to trailer level by using a dock leveler. To accommodate the newer low-profile trailers, dock levelers are now available in lengths of 12 feet. For warehouse trucks to have straight-in, straight-out, full-width access to the largest loads on high-cube trailers, a minimum of 8-foot long dock levelers will be required. Another device, called a dual dock, also lowers the truck to the level of the trailer bed.

• Truck Levelers (**Figure 3.8**). The other approach is to bring the trailer to dock level. Portable wheel ramps are one possibility, but a safer, more flexible, and increasingly popular method is a truck leveler, which raises the trailer to the dock level. Today's truck levelers come surface-mounted for easy installa-

Figure 3.9. Mechanized Receiving with Elevated Sortation System

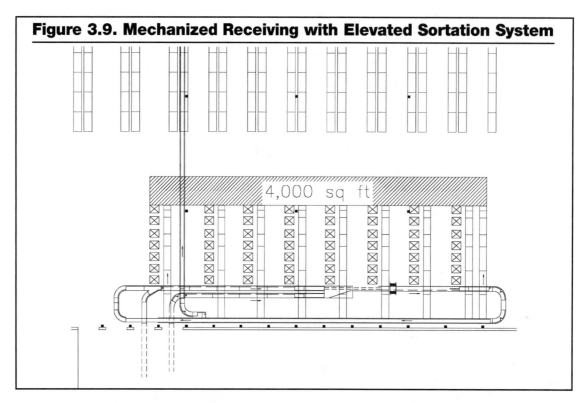

4,000 sq ft

Figure 3.10. Sample Dock Layout with Staging Areas Defined

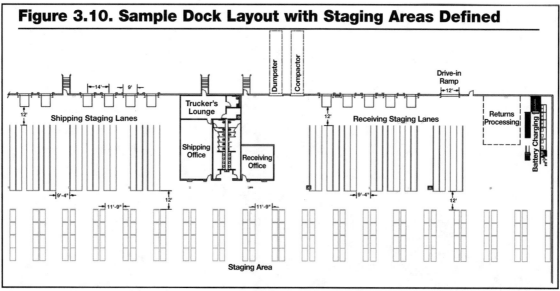

tion and simple service, with no pit, trench, or drain. Low collapsed height makes it easy for trailers to back into position.[6]

Step 3. Determining the Size and Placement of the Staging Areas. The size of the staging area is dependent on the types of operations for receiving and shipping. A high degree of checking and inspection will directly increase space requirements. Floor-loaded shipments may have to be palletized before storage. Conveyors may be used to increase throughput. **Figure 3.9** shows a receiving layout using an elevated sortation system to sort and palletize inbound floor-loaded receipts. Cross docking operations may require sorting and consolidation of pallet loads before shipping. Because of the nature of their business, mail-order operations and Internet sales anticipate a large number of returns. Space will be required to receive these returns. The type, frequency, size, number of ship-to locations, delivery sequence, and shipping and loading time of products also affect staging space requirements. The rule-of-thumb for sizing a regular receiving staging area is to allow the square footage to equal the footprint surface of the average receipt vehicle multiplied by the number of receipts anticipated at peak activity plus a factor for access aisles. This allows the receipts to be off-loaded upon arrival and held in a controlled receiving area until they can be inspected and accepted into inventory. Similarly, an operation that requires shipments to be consolidated must allow a shipping staging area equal to the square footage of the peak number of outbound pallets plus a factor for access aisles.[7]

For example, a 40-foot long and 8-foot wide trailer has a footprint of 320 square feet. A full load carries double-stacked pallets with heights of up to 8 feet. At peak, the number of receipts is calculated at an average of 15 trailers per day. Thus, a receiving staging area of 4,800 square feet (320 sq. ft. X 15) will be required. Adding 50% for access aisles, the required receiving staging area is calculated at 7,200 square feet. Using racks in the staging areas can further reduce the footprint.

Aisles in Staging. Before laying out the staging area, a main aisle of 8 to 10 feet from the end of the dock levelers should be kept clear for movement of pallet jacks and other vehicles unloading or loading pallets. If lift trucks are used, a main aisle of 10 to 12 feet is recommended. Following the staging area, another main aisle of 12 to 15 feet should separate the dock area from the storage area to reduce aisle contention between the dock and storage operations. **Figure 3.10** illustrates a sample layout of a dock area.

Step 4. Specifying Dock Equipment Needs. There are various kinds of equipment for moving material on the dock area. Following are some considerations for dock equipment:

• The actual dock door is a big consideration. A dock door is a constant target for lift trucks moving in confined areas. Whenever possible, knock-out doors are recommended. These relatively new doors are designed to "knock-out" and retain their shape when they sustain a blow. When loads smack into the door panel, spring-loaded pins instantly slide out of the guide track. A quick tug on the panel slides the pins back into place, and the door is as good as new.[8]

• Lift trucks should be equipped with seat belts, backup alarms, horns, overhead guards, tilt indicators, and a fire extinguisher. Drivers must be trained to ensure safe driving practices. They must have certificates attesting that they have completed a training program.

• Pedestrian traffic should be restricted in the dock area with a clearly marked walkway.

Guardrails should define the pedestrian walkway. Convex mirrors should be installed at blind corners.

• Vehicle restraint systems should be installed at the docks, which will ensure that there is no accidental pull-away by a trailer while it is being serviced. Wheel chocks also serve this purpose and are inexpensive, but they are not as reliable as trailer restraining devices, particularly in the snow. These restraints range from simple mechanical devices to sophisticated electronic ones with engagement warning lights for dock personnel and trailer drivers. They should be effective in all weather conditions. Dock personnel should be trained to verify that the vehicle restraints are always engaged.

Figure 3.11. Safety Lip Truck Barrier

Reprinted with permission from Rite-Hite Corporation, Milwaukee, WI.

• If wheel chocks are used, the drivers are typically responsible for placing them and the dock workers must check them. Automatic wheel chocks are also available.

• Dock levelers that will provide a gentle grade into trailers of all heights should be chosen. They should be able to service 8.5-foot-wide trailers. Leveler capacity must be adequate to handle all load weights. Dock levelers should have full-range toe-guards, ramp free-fall protection, automatic recycling, safety stops, and a safety lip to prevent lift trucks from driving off of open docks. **Figure 3.11** shows a safety lip truck barrier.

• Proper lighting is essential to fast, safe shipping/receiving operations, and dock lights should be installed for use inside trailers. Trailer approach guide lights on both sides of the dock doors would be helpful as guides for night operations.

• Weather sealing is advised for operations that are located in cold weather climates. It saves energy and increases safety by preventing rain, snow, dirt, and debris from blowing on the docks where they might cause slippage and lift truck skids. Placing canopies over docks also serves as protection from inclement weather.

Safety on the Dock. With its high concentration of activities, the dock is the area where most accidents are likely to happen. Dock accidents can be a significant cost factor if the proper

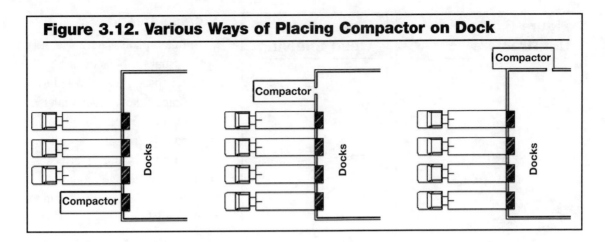

Figure 3.12. Various Ways of Placing Compactor on Dock

equipment is not utilized. Costs are both direct, such as compensation benefits and medical treatment, and indirect, such as production losses, the value of spoiled or damaged products, and equipment repair. Proper training of employees, proper selection and maintenance of equipment, and well-designed operating procedures are necessary for smooth shipping/receiving operations. According to OSHA, all dock employees must attend a comprehensive dock training program. They must be trained in the use of all dock equipment (dock levelers, vehicle restraints, driving rules, etc.) and in safety/emergency procedures. Dock equipment must be maintained to ensure proper operation and to avoid malfunctions.

Step 5. Allowing Space on the Dock for Other Functions. There are other functions that may be located in the dock area. Some of these include the following:

• A trucker's lounge that includes desk space, a pay phone, vending machines, and a rest room, with a minimum area of 120 square feet and 20-plus square feet for each additional driver.[9] (This lounge should have limited access to the dock area.)

• Staging of trash and recyclables, such as corrugated items, including an additional dock door position devoted to a dumpster or trash compactor. If possible, run the compactor opening through the wall, as shown in **Figure 3.12**, to save valuable dock doors and improve security.

• Battery charging areas.

• Packing areas and storage of packing material.

• Receiving and shipping offices.

• Pallet storage, including scrap and broken pallets.

These areas are essential to overall warehouse operations but should be planned and maintained properly so as not to impede dock operations. Docks should not be used as a "temporary" burial ground for excess inventory, obsolete equipment, defective goods, and other non-dock related material. The use of mezzanines, racks, and shelving for some of these functions may minimize square footage without compromising efficient dock operations.

Figure 3.13. Bin Drawers

Figure 3.14. Open Shelving

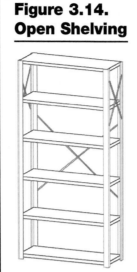

Figure 3.15. Mobile Shelving

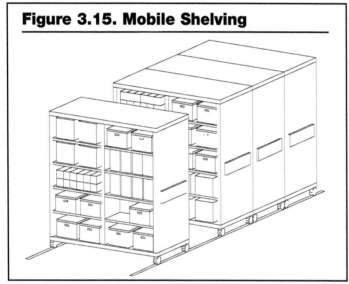

Storage Area

In a typical warehouse, it is not unusual for 60% or more of the total space to be devoted to the storage function. An understanding of the components of this space is critical. The following section lists and describes the different storage modules and the material handling equipment available.

Storage Modules. There are various types of storage modules for different sizes and volumes of product in inventory. In this section, we make a distinction between small items that do not make up a unit load — e.g., loose pieces, cases, and totes — and items that are handled by a piece of material handling equipment as a unit load, such as cases on a pallet.

Less Than a Pallet Load Per Item. For items in the warehouse that do not make up a unit load, possible storage modules include bin drawers, shelving, flow racks, carousels, and automated mini-load systems.

• Bin drawers (**Figure 3.13**). These are used to store small items, such as screws, semiconductors, and gaskets. The products may be stored loose or in cartons. Dividers within each drawer maintain product integrity while promoting efficient use of space.

• Shelving (**Figure 3.14**). Products placed on shelving can be stored in individual bins, cases, or totes. The most common type of shelf is open shelving. This type of shelving has no back and side panels. This allows for flexibility in storing irregular-shaped items. Conversely, closed shelving has back and side panels. This shelving is more aesthetically pleasing and provides more protection to the products. Both types of shelving come in many sizes and load capacities. Mobile shelving (**Figure 3.15**) is another type. Mobile shelving requires only one or two aisles for several

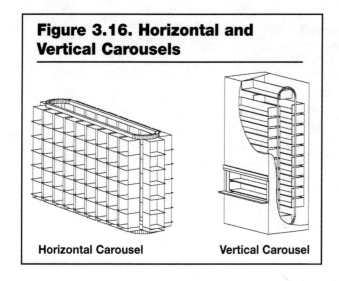

Figure 3.16. Horizontal and Vertical Carousels

Horizontal Carousel   Vertical Carousel

rows, greatly increasing storage density. The shelving rides on a rail structure so that the aisle can be created only when a product needs to be accessed.

• Case flow racks. These are inclined shelving racks of various depths. These present a large number of items in a short distance. Products are replenished at the raised back of a shelf, and they flow through the rack structure on rollers propelled by the force of gravity. Products are retrieved at the lower front end of the shelf. This type of module is widely used in order picking.

• Carousels. Carousels consist of either horizontally or vertically revolving bins or shelf units. As opposed to the two previous modules where the worker goes to the product, the carousel brings the product to the worker for storage or retrieval. Carousels are also typically used in order picking. See **Figure 3.16**.

• Miniload AS/RS. One type of automated module for the storage and retrieval of cartons and totes is the miniload automated storage/retrieval system (AS/RS). This system consists of rack shelving, a storage and retrieval crane, and a pick-up or drop-off station. Information downloaded from the computer signals the storage and retrieval machine to pick the correct tote and bring it to the drop-off station. Inventory is automatically updated. This miniload system makes efficient use of vertical space since it has the capability of storing products many levels high.

Pallet Loads. For pallet loads of items, there are two basic configurations: (1) floor storage and (2) rack storage.

Floor storage, also known as bulk storage, is the practice of stacking pallets on top of each other in various heights and depths on the floor. It is the least expensive and most flexible configuration since there is no storage equipment to purchase and install. It also provides very dense storage. The disadvantage is that its application is limited since all pallets in a lane must be the same. Only large quantities and fast-moving SKUs can be stored this way. In addition, the pallet loads must be able to stack on top of each other without damage. Stacking frames are available to alleviate this issue, but with the added cost per frame, it may not be as cost effective as racking. Finally, with bulk storage, periodic re-warehousing is required to maintain the cubic utilization of storage space.

Rack storage is composed of beams and uprights in varying lengths and widths within which pallet loads can be stored. It allows for better selectivity and FIFO (first in-first out) controls as each pallet is more accessible than in bulk storage. There are different types of rack storage. These include:

• Single Deep Racks or Selective Racks. In these racks, the storage is one pallet deep and each pallet is accessible. One aisle serves a row of selective racks on each side of the aisle. Selective racks provide the most flexible unit load storage system, as any unit can be stored or retrieved without handling any others. The drawback is that it requires the most aisles.

• Double Deep Racks. These racks are made up of two selective racks placed one behind the other. Depth of storage is two pallets, and a deep-reach lift truck is used to handle a pallet in the rear slot. It is desirable to store the same item in both the front and rear slots to avoid double handling, but different items can be stored at each level.

• Drive-In or Drive-Through Racks. In these racks, pallets can be stored any number deep with access from a single aisle. In practice, the depth of storage is usually limited to six to eight pallets. The lift truck must enter the rack to handle the pallets in inner slots. In drive-in racks, the storage and retrieval of pallets is done from the same end of the rack using the same aisle. In drive-through racks, storage and retrieval are from different aisles. The same item should be stored in a lane, both in depth and height, to avoid additional handling. Although it offers deep storage and high stacking, it requires standardized pallets in good condition and demands substantial skill from the lift truck operator.

• Push-Back Racks. These are similar in concept to drive-in racks except that the lift truck does not have to enter the rack lanes to store or retrieve pallets. Pallets are placed on nesting trolleys at each storage level, and the lift truck pushes them back into the racks using the adjacent pallets. Since the lift truck stays in the aisle, the handling is faster than for drive-in racks. Storage depth is limited to five pallets. Push-back racks are more expensive than drive-in racks and may be justified for applications such as freezers, where space savings and speed are important.

• Cantilever Racks. These racks are used to store long, bulky, and unusually shaped items. A different SKU is stored on each level. They come in variable arm lengths, and wire decking can be installed for additional support.

• Pallet Flow Racks. In these racks, pallets are replenished from one end and retrieved from the other end. The pallets move from the back to the front on conveyors. These racks are suitable for high-volume order picking for a limited number of SKUs.

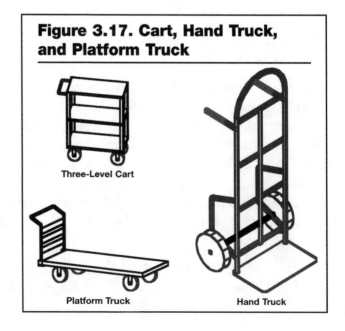

Figure 3.17. Cart, Hand Truck, and Platform Truck

Three-Level Cart

Platform Truck

Hand Truck

• Mobile Rack. These racks are movable and eliminate fixed aisles. Access aisles can be created as needed.

Heights to which pallets can be stored in these modules will depend on the lifting capabilities of the lift trucks and the clear stacking height in the building.

Material Handling Equipment. Many different types of material handling equipment, with a wide range of operating characteristics, are available to store and retrieve material from various storage modules.

Less Than a Pallet Load Per Item. For cases and totes stored in shelving and bin drawers, handling equipment such as carts, hand trucks, and platform trucks (**Figure 3.17**) are commonly used.

• Carts. These can be described as shelving on four wheels. Aisle clearance depends on the size of the cart. Most carts for use with shelving are able to work in 36-inch aisles.

• Hand trucks. With two wheels, hand trucks are less stable and transport fewer items in one trip. These trucks are typically used in moving heavy, irregularly shaped objects.

• Platform trucks. Platform trucks are usually larger than carts but have only one level or deck, called a platform. They can transport a large number of items at a time.

Pallet Loads. For handling pallet loads, different types of lift trucks in common use are:

Figure 3.18. Electric Sit-Down Counterbalanced Truck

Reprinted with permission from Hyster Company, Greenville, NC.

Figure 3.19. Stand-Up Counterbalanced Truck

Reprinted with permission from Raymond of New Jersey LLC, Union, NJ.

• Counterbalanced Lift Trucks. These trucks are versatile vehicles. They can operate efficiently on docks to load or unload trailers, and they are most suitable for going up and down ramps. They can handle pallets and unit loads in various storage modules. Their operation is similar to an automobile and therefore easier to learn than many other types of lift trucks. They can be powered by electricity, diesel fuel, gasoline, propane, or natural gas. They can have pneumatic, cushioned, or solid tires. They generally require aisle widths starting at approximately 12 feet, depending on the make and capacity. Depending on the model, lift height can be up to about 20 feet. The driver operates the truck from either a sitting (**Figure 3.18**) or standing position (**Figure 3.19**), depending on the model. A stand-up counterbalanced truck is usually more expensive than a sit-down model, but it can operate in an aisle width of approximately 10 feet.

Figure 3.20. Walkie Stacker

Reprinted with permission from Crown Equipment Corporation, New Bremen, OH.

• Walkie Stacker (**Figure 3.20**). An operator steers this truck from a walking position behind the vehicle. These trucks are recommended for short travel distances, low vertical storage height, and low throughput operations. Walkie stackers can be either counterbalanced or straddle. The counterbalanced types are longer and require a larger aisle.

• Reach Lift Trucks (**Figure 3.21**). These trucks can handle pallets efficiently in aisles as

Figure 3.21. Narrow Aisle Reach Truck

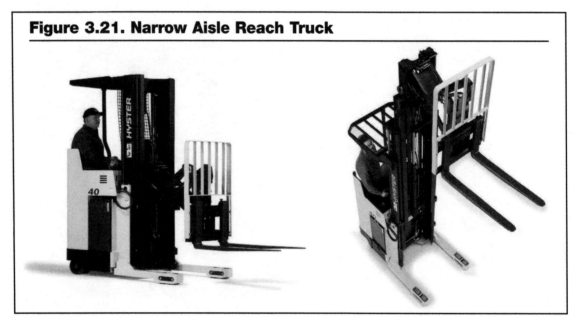

Reprinted with permission from Hyster Company, Greenville, NC.

Figure 3.22. Operator-Up Turret (Swing Reach) Truck

Reprinted with permission from Hyster Company, Greenville, NC.

narrow as 8 feet and can lift loads to a height of about 32 feet. The pantograph reach mechanism allows the forks to extend and store a pallet in a single deep rack. In some trucks, the mast moves forward instead of using the pantograph. Other models have forks that extend out to the load instead of a pantograph. The driver operates the truck in a standing position. It is only available in electric models. It is not as versatile as a counterbalanced truck and is not recommended for truck loading and unloading because of the small wheels on the outriggers and the mast height.

• Deep Reach Lift Trucks. These trucks have reach mechanisms that can extend to a depth of two pallets. They can store or retrieve pallet loads in a double deep rack storage system. They can lift

Figure 3.23. Articulating Truck

Reprinted with permission from Landoll Corporation, Marysville, KS.

Figure 3.24. Side-Loader Truck

Reprinted with permission from Raymond of New Jersey LLC, Union, NJ.

Figure 3.25. Omni-Directional Truck

Reprinted with permission from Airtrax Inc. Hammonton, NJ.

loads to approximately 32 feet and require aisles that are at least nine feet wide. Other operating characteristics are similar to the reach lift truck.

• Swing Reach or Turret Trucks (**Figure 3.22**). These trucks can operate in aisles of approximately 6 feet (load to load) and lift loads to a height of over 40 feet. The trucks do not turn in the storage aisle but the fork mechanism on the masts can turn 90 degrees left and right, to store or remove pallets from racks. They usually require a guidance device, typically rails or a wire in the floor to guide them through the narrow aisles. Technologies such as tape, remote sensors, and chemicals are also used, but are less common. These trucks are cumbersome to maneuver outside the storage aisles. They operate primarily in selective rack systems, but they can operate in double deep racks. Due to the higher lifting heights and narrower aisles, these vehicles often require "superflat" floors. A variation of these trucks are "swing mast trucks," whereby the mast swings to store or remove pallets from the racks. Their limitation is that the mast can swing only to one side, so that the trucks must turn around to work on the other side of the aisle.

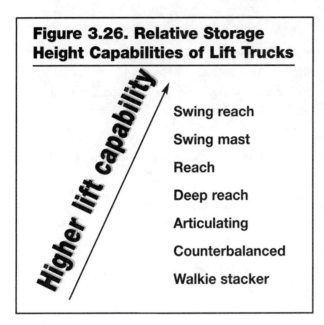

Figure 3.26. Relative Storage Height Capabilities of Lift Trucks

Higher lift capability →

Swing reach

Swing mast

Reach

Deep reach

Articulating

Counterbalanced

Walkie stacker

However, they can work in narrower aisles of 5 feet (load to load).

• Articulating Trucks (**Figure 3.23**). These trucks are relatively new to the market. They work in aisles as narrow as 6.5 feet. The entire mast swings to handle pallets from either side (unlike the swing mast truck) and can be used in a wide variety of applications.

In addition to these, there are several highly specialized vehicles for handling pallet loads, including:

• Side-Loader Trucks (**Figure 3.24**). These trucks are used mostly for long units, such as lumber and pipes. Aisle sizes are similar to that of a turret truck. Certain models can be used for regular pallet handling.

• Omni-Directional Trucks (**Figure 3.25**). This relatively new truck has specialized wheels that can move in any direction without turning the entire vehicle. It is one of a few trucks that

Figure 3.27. Material Handling Equipment and Appropriate Storage Module

	Selective rack	Double deep rack	Cantilever rack	Drive-in (or through) rack	Bulk floor storage	Push-back rack	Pallet flow rack	Docks to storage	Load/ unload trucks
Counterbalanced	3	0	2	3	3	3	3	3	3
Narrow aisle reach	3	1	2	2	2	3	3	3	1
Deep reach	3	3	2	2	2	3	3	3	1
Swing mast	3	0	2	1	2	1	3	2	2
Swing reach	3	0	1	0	0	3	3	1	0
Articulating	3	0	2	1	2	2	3	3	2
Side loader	2	0	3	0	0	0	0	2	0
Walkie stacker	3	0	2	3	3	1	2	2	1
Order picker	3	2	3	0	1	1	1	2	0
Pallet jack	3	1	0	0	1	0	0	3	3

Key: 3 = optimal; 2 = OK, not optimal; 1 = in a pinch; 0 = don't do it

can move sideways while facing front.

• Stacker Cranes. These are the handling components of an automated storage/retrieval system. These systems are a combination of pallet racks as high as 130 feet and cranes that are designed to store and retrieve pallets from such heights. The machines move along floor and/or roof-mounted tracks in aisles only six to eight inches wider than the load. They can be either automated or operated by a person aboard.

Figure 3.26 lists the relative storage height capabilities of the different lift trucks with the swing reach truck achieving the maximum.

The storage modules described here apply to unit loads that are on pallets. Other common handling mediums include skids and slipsheets. However, they may require special attachments for trucks and decking on pallet racks.

Figure 3.27 is a chart that rates the appropriateness of the above trucks to specific storage modules and other warehouse operations. Pallet jacks, order picker trucks, and conveyors are other examples of material handling equipment, which will be discussed in greater detail in the section on order processing, where they have greater applicability than in the storage area. The two simplest machines are the walkie stacker and the pallet jack. While they are less expensive, their optimal use is limited to a few handling situations. The most versatile machine is the counterbalanced truck. The most specialized and the least versatile is the side loader.

This discussion of storage modules and handling equipment does not include highly customized systems such as a multi-pallet deep AS/RS system with a Rack Entry Module (also called a "Mole"), which is capital intensive and, typically, can only be economically justified in such applications as freezers, where construction and operating savings can offset high equipment costs.

Developing the Design Criteria. The most common problem is determining appropriate storage modules to use with a company's inventory profile. How many pallets should be on the floor or in five-deep, drive-through racks? How much space is needed for storage? The following approach should assist in developing the design criteria and in generating alternative storage methods. Using computer spreadsheet and database tools will be helpful in organizing and analyzing raw data. Developing the design criteria includes the following steps:

1. Defining the objectives and scope of the storage analysis

2. Collecting the data

3. Organizing the data into groups that make it easy to analyze

4. Profiling the data

5. Projecting to the design year.

Step 1. Defining the Objectives and Scope of the Storage Analysis. This step defines the purpose of the analysis and the extent of the study. The objective may be to redesign an existing operation or to start with a clean slate and create a new facility for a storage operation. There may be a need to reuse an existing warehouse management system (WMS) and warehouse equipment. Perhaps the storage of only one specific product family is to be studied. These limits have to be defined to facilitate collecting information, to rule out certain alternatives, to focus efforts on critical parts of the operation, and to guide the overall design process.

Step 2. Collecting the Data. The following basic information is required to set up a spreadsheet model to determine storage requirements (other analyses may require more or less information):

Design Year. This is usually provided by upper management as the maximum number of years that they can "accurately" forecast business trends. Some companies may have a four-year order backlog allowing them to forecast well into the future, and some companies can provide fairly reliable forecasts up to five years. Beyond five years, there may exist a compelling need to reevaluate the operation. Depending on the objectives of the study, the design year may depend on available capacity of an existing building or a future property acquisition. A requirement to sign a 10-year lease on a build-to-suit facility may force estimating design year requirements beyond company sales projections. In the case of an existing facility, there is only a limited amount of space for expansion. However, a company may contemplate future property acquisitions and may want to determine how far into the future the new property can accommodate its business.

Growth Factors for Each Year as a Percentage of Volume. This may be based on sales forecasts provided by the marketing department. Care should be taken when basing growth percentages on dollar figures, as it may have no direct relation to cubic volume.

Time Period. The usual practice is to design storage equipment to accommodate peak requirements. Exceptions do occur depending on the duration and the "height" of the peak period relative to the rest of the year. Activity may be extremely erratic with peaks that occur for only a short period of time and vary greatly during the year. During these periods, additional analyses may be required to determine whether public warehousing will be required for overflow stock.

Product Properties and Special Storage Requirements. This describes the products to be stored. Product properties should include SKU number, product description, pieces per carton, cartons per pallet, cube per carton, and weights. For storage analyses, cube per carton is crucial information, though it is often ignored or inaccurately recorded in a database. An SKU may be as small as a box of paper clips or as large as a refrigerator. Some items may have special storage requirements, such as a clean room, hazmat guidelines, a freezer, or a secure vault. Certain storage rules relating to lot control — such as FIFO — may apply and may have to be considered. Another essential data requirement relating to product properties is the load characteristic. Can pallets be stacked on top of each other? If so, how high can they be stacked? Pallets with drums and cases of canned food can be stacked four to five pallets high. Pallets with cases of loose toys may not stack at all. An important product property is the size of a unit load. This dimension should include the size of a pallet, including any overhang. Required clearances for storage and handling equipment should be determined. Another consideration is how the unit load is contained. Wooden pallets are still the favorite medium among warehouses today. The Grocery

Manufacturers Association (GMA) has outlined detailed specifications for pallets in the industry. A typical GMA pallet is 48 inches deep by 40 inches wide, is not more than 6 inches high, and may have a four-way entry. However, other products may be on different-sized pallets; on skids, slipsheets, or wire frames; or in drums that may require special lift truck attachments.

Peak Inventory by SKU for the Specified Time Period. The most effective listing of inventory shows each SKU with the corresponding inventory in cubic feet or in pallet quantities. It is surprising how few companies keep inventory information of these important quantities. Databases may show inventory in pieces or in dollars. These numbers should be converted to unit load quantities.

Inventory and Movement Data. Inventory data may be adjusted for peaks in the movement data. There are instances, however, where inventory may have peaks that are not the same as movement. The key is to collect adequate inventory samples at several points in time. By collecting these data, cyclical trends, peaks, consistencies, and opportunities for smoothing can be identified. It will also help in making decisions for peak inventory overflow. Movement data will identify products with high movement that enter and leave the warehouse at a fast rate. Products with high movement should be stored in dense and efficient storage and retrieval modules close to the shipping areas. Products with slow movement can be situated farther away from the docks. If inventory data is not available, the movement data can be converted to inventory data by using either of the following formulas:

$$\text{Average Inventory} = \frac{\text{Annual Sales or Movement}}{\text{Turnover Rate Per Year}}$$

$$\text{Average Inventory} = \text{Annual Sales or Movement} \times \text{Year(s) of Inventory}$$

The turnover rate is the number of times in a year that the inventory has been converted to sales. The year(s) of inventory is the reciprocal of the turnover rate. It is usually expressed in terms of the number of weeks or months of inventory required to support the sale of a product. Be wary of turnover rates that are expressed in dollars ($). Applying dollar turnover rates to the above formulas can cause distortions. If neither inventory nor movement data is available, then a physical count of the products currently in stock will be required for the analysis.

Throughput Rate. Throughput rate refers to product movement in and out of the storage area for a specified time period. It is used to determine the pieces of handling equipment required to move units from the receiving docks to storage, from storage to forward pick, and from forward pick to shipping.

Step 3. *Organizing the Data into Groups that Make it Easy to Analyze.* After collecting the data, it is important to organize the information into groups that make it easy to analyze. Products requiring a controlled environment are usually one of the first groups to be set apart from the rest of the SKUs. Other grouping factors include whether products are to be picked in pallet, unit load, full case, or broken case quantities; specific equipment that can store and handle the products; and how and where products flow through the warehouse. Awkward or large SKUs cannot go through a conveyor sortation system and must be grouped and stored separately.

Step 4. Profiling the Data. For each group, a profile of the inventory is created. An inventory profile is the frequency of SKUs that correspond to a specific range of pallet or cube inventory per SKU. SKUs with high inventories are better suited for storage in dense systems, such as floor storage and drive-in racks. SKUs with low volumes may be stored in single deep racks. SKUs with volumes that are significantly less than a pallet are recommended for storage in shelving or drawers, depending on size. **Figure 3.28** shows applicable storage modules for various ranges of pallets per SKU.

A movement profile is a frequency distribution by SKU that identifies the popularity or degree of demand within a specific range. Some high-throughput SKUs should be stored in pallet flow racks, which are rack structures where a pallet is put in on one end of the lane and retrieved at the other end. This type of structure is best for FIFO movement. Strict FIFO and/or lot control limits or eliminates the applicability of drive-in racks and deep floor storage. Many companies treat an SKU with two lot or batch numbers as two distinct SKUs requiring different storage facings.

After creating profiles of movement and inventory, items at the "bottom of the barrel" should be examined. First, they should identify slow-moving, excess, or obsolete inventory and consider eliminating it from further analysis. **Figure 3.29** illustrates a sample analysis of excess inventory. Based on the sample data, management has identified Item No. 4 for further analysis.

Figure 3.28. Sample Inventory Profile and Corresponding Storage Modules

| Range of No. of Pallets Per Item | No. of Items | Total No. of Pallets | Average No. of Pallets Per Item | Applicable Storage Module X = Preferred Storage Module O = Workable But Not Preferred | | | | | | |
| | | | | Pallet Load | | | | Less than Pallet Load | | |
				Floor Storage	Double Drive-In Racks	Single Deep Racks	Case Deep Racks	Flow Racks	Shelves	Bin Drawers
>100	2	350	175	X	X	O	O			
51 to 100	18	1,100	61	X	X	O	O			
21 to 50	40	1,000	25	X	X	X	O			
11 to 20	160	2,200	14	O	O	X	O			
6 to 10	330	2,300	7	O	O	X	X			
2 to 5	500	1,600	3			O	X			
0.5 to 1	750	750	1				X	X		
0.25 to 0.49	900	270	0.3				O	X	X	
0.24 to 0.001	1,100	65	0.06					X	X	O
0.001 or less	200	0.10	0.0005						O	X

Figure 3.29. Sample Excess Inventory Analysis

Item No.	Avg. Inv.	Annual Sales	Inv. Turns	Weeks Supply	Target Turns	Cube/ Unit	Inv. Cube	Target Inv. Cube	Excess Inv. Cube
1	2,000	26,000	13.0	4.0	2	0.05	100	650	0
2	1,000	2,000	2.0	26.0	2	0.18	180	180	0
3	800	1,200	1.5	34.7	2	0.22	176	132	44
4	1,200	1,200	1.0	52.0	2	0.85	1,020	510	510
5	300	100	0.3	156.0	2	0.66	198	33	165
6	400	40	0.1	520.0	2	0.01	4	0.2	3.8

$$\frac{\text{Annual Sales}}{52 \text{ Weeks}} = \text{Sales Per Week} \qquad \frac{\text{Average Inventory}}{\text{Sales Per Week}} = \text{Weeks Supply}$$

Marketing plans have calculated the target inventory cube for Item No. 4 to be set at 510 cubic feet. Current inventory for that item, however, is 1,020 cubic feet — an excess inventory cube of 510 cubic feet. This excess inventory should be marked down and sold, disposed of, or moved offsite to make room for faster moving items.

A warehouse may not always have enough space, but the problem can be improved by creating and periodically reviewing profiles.

Step 5. Projecting to the Design Year. This step uses historical data to forecast future changes in the business. Growth factors are used as a percentage of volume. When the trend is linear and you are only concerned with the final design-year projections, the following shortcut can be used. (Again, this formula applies only to a linear growth trend.)

$$X_Y = X_1 \times (1 + A)^{Y-1}$$

where:

Y	=	Years into the Future
X_Y	=	Volume During the Design Year
X	=	Volume During Year One
A	=	Percentage Growth Per Year

For example: A company may have a current inventory of 500 pallets (Year 1). Projected inventory four years into the future (Year 5) based on a 3% annual growth in volume is determined as follows.

$$X_5 \quad = \quad 500 \text{ pallets} \times (1 + 0.03)^{5-1} \quad = \quad 563 \text{ pallets}$$

Generating Alternative Storage Designs. Completing the data analysis should provide the following design criteria for the design year:

- Projected pallet and/or case inventory and movement profiles

- The total number of pallet and/or case positions required

- The possible storage modules

- The total number of items or SKUs

- The stacking height and column spacing (if an existing building).

Different storage alternatives can then be developed based on the design criteria above. This section can be divided into two major steps:

1. Developing general storage concepts and layouts

2. Developing space, labor, and equipment requirements.

Step 1. Developing General Storage Concepts. Understanding the design year inventory profile helps to determine the appropriate storage concept. When designing a new facility, there is a wide range of alternatives. In an existing facility, certain restrictions limit the number of alternatives.

Storage heights. In an existing building, the clear height of the ceiling determines the storage height. Depending on the merchandise stored, underwriters and fire codes may require at least 18 inches of clearance between the top of the load and the sprinkler heads, but this depends on the municipality. The underwriter and local fire department should be checked for their requirements. Aside from local fire codes and regulations, factors affecting storage height include equipment constraints, unit load heights, and pallet rack beam dimensions. Other considerations for storage heights are that:

- Floor stacks are limited by product stackability

- Racking can extend to greater heights, but the lift trucks required get more specialized

- Weight of load that can be lifted to the higher levels is reduced as the truck gets "de-rated"

- Deep storage is limited in height due to lack of deep

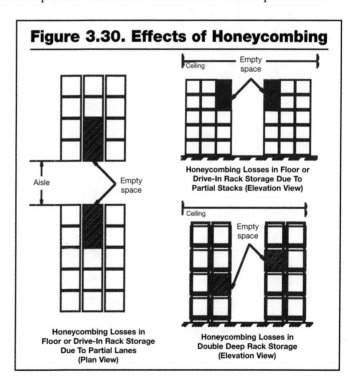

Figure 3.30. Effects of Honeycombing

Empty space

Ceiling

Empty space

Aisle — Empty space

Honeycombing Losses in Floor or Drive-In Rack Storage Due To Partial Stacks (Elevation View)

Ceiling

Empty space

Honeycombing Losses in Floor or Drive-In Rack Storage Due To Partial Lanes (Plan View)

Honeycombing Losses in Double Deep Rack Storage (Elevation View)

Figure 3.31. Calculating Effects of Honeycombing And Storage Utilization

How to calculate the utilization factor (Honeycombing):

- Start with pallets in inventory (per SKU or per lot)

- Divide by pallets per lane = Lanes/SKU

- On the average, one lane is half full

- For example, if there are three lanes for one SKU:

    - 2 lanes @ 100%

    - 1 lane @ 50%

    - Weighted average is 83%

Other rules of thumb utilization factors:

- Single deep (selective) rack — 90%

- Double deep rack — 80%

- Drive-in rack, bulk storage — 65% (highly variable)

Approximate Utilization Sample:

- 1 Lane/SKU — 50% utilization

- 2 Lanes/SKU — 75%

- 3 Lanes/SKU — 83%

- 4 Lanes/SKU — 87%

- 5 Lanes/SKU — 90%

- 6 Lanes/SKU — 92%

---

reach capabilities at higher levels and the force required to use push-back racks

- Blind access limits productivity at upper levels of deep reach systems.

Honeycombing. It is important to factor the effects of honeycombing into the pallet capacity of the storage area. Honeycombing is the wasted space brought about by partially filled rows and stacks. Pallets of other items should not be placed in these empty positions because they will block the first item's accessibility. **Figure 3.30** shows a diagram of honeycombing in storage modules.

The utilization of the storage modules decreases as storage becomes more dense and honeycombing increases. To compensate for the decrease of usable pallet positions, a storage utilization allowance should be used. **Figure 3.31** shows common storage utilization allowances. For example, when inventory calls for storing 100 pallets in double deep racks, the storage utilization allowance is approximately 80%. This means 125 pallet positions (100 ÷ 0.80) should be provided. With this number of pallet positions and only 80% utilization due to honeycombing, there is still capacity for the required 100 pallets (125 x 0.8).

Column Spacing. Feasible storage system combinations should not only satisfy storage capacity requirements but also space and building requirements. Designing the columns within the space between back-to-back rows of racks maximizes the number of available storage positions. This is in contrast to having a column within a vertical section of racks and losing storage positions. **Figure 3.32** shows the effect of column spacing on single deep racks.

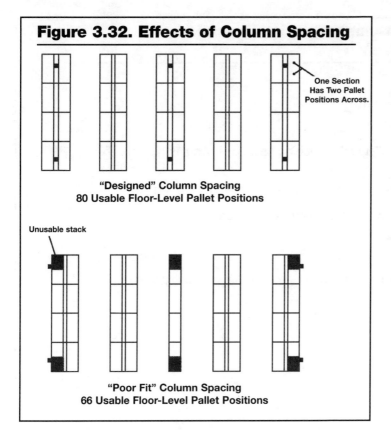

Figure 3.32. Effects of Column Spacing

One Section Has Two Pallet Positions Across.

"Designed" Column Spacing
80 Usable Floor-Level Pallet Positions

Unusable stack

"Poor Fit" Column Spacing
66 Usable Floor-Level Pallet Positions

Different types of storage modules provide varying degrees of space efficiency within certain column spacings. When designing a new facility, it becomes critical to determine the best column spacing for the majority of the storage modules. To determine optimal column spacing in the direction perpendicular to rack rows and aisles for a particular rack/truck combination, add the aisle width to the width of a back-to-back storage module bay (including pallet overhang, if any). The optimal column spacing is a multiple of that number, plus the column size. For example: Assuming the use of 48-inch by 40-inch pallets, 12-inch by 12-inch columns, 42-inch-deep rack sections, 8-foot beams, 3-inch-wide uprights, and a minimum of 12-inch back-to-back spacing between rack sections, **Figure 3.33** illustrates how to calculate the optimal column facing perpendicular to rack rows and aisles for a narrow aisle reach truck in selective rack modules. **Figure 3.34** illustrates how to calculate the optimal column spacing parallel to aisles.

The Effect of Aisles on Space Utilization. Illustrated in **Figure 3.35** are the different storage modules, the corresponding material handling equipment, and the workable aisle allowances and lift heights. A counterbalanced lift truck is workable with any storage module except for double deep racks. Maximum lift height is approximately 23 feet, with storage aisles ranging from 10 to 12 feet wide. **Figure 3.36** shows a comparison of the different storage densities with different rack and truck alternatives. The narrow aisle reach truck/drive-in rack combination (F) offers the highest storage space utilization for facilities with limited storage space. Conversely, the combinations with wider aisles (A and B) will support higher throughput operations. Cross aisles are paths of travel perpendicular to the storage aisles. Widths of cross aisles depend on the amount of traffic expected and the type of equipment that has to turn in these aisles. For most trucks, a 12-foot cross aisle may be adequate for high-traffic areas where vehicles continually pass each other. Some very narrow aisle (VNA) trucks require a cross aisle of 18 feet as a turning radius from rows of storage modules.

Figure 3.33. Optimal Column Spacing Example (Perpendicular to Aisles)

Assumptions:

- Building columns are 12-inch square

- Reach truck works best in 8'-6" clear aisles (or 9' beam to beam)

- Back-to-back single deep pallet rack, including pallet overhang, is typically 8'-6" (or 8' beam to beam)

- The length of each center-to-center bay of racks is 17' (8'-6" + 8'-6")

- Optimal column spacing is 35' or 52' (in the direction perpendicular to the rack aisles):

    - (17'/bay x 2 bays) + 1' (for column clearance) = 35' column spacing

    - (17'/bay x 3 bays) + 1' (for column clearance) = 52' column spacing

Sample Layout:

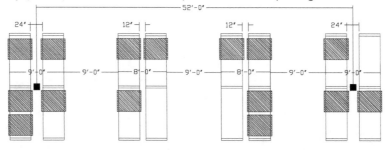

Figure 3.34. Optimal Column Spacing Example (Parallel to Aisles)

Facts:

- In the direction parallel to the rack rows, the column spacing is less critical

- The optimal column spacing is a number divisible by the centerline distance between rack sections

Example:

- 96"-long beams

- 3"-wide uprights

- The optimal column spacing in this direction must be a multiple of the total of these two distances. Since 96" + 3" equals 99", optimal column spacing includes 33'-0" (4 x 99"), 41'-3" (5 x 99"), and 49'-6" (6 x 99").

Sample Layout:

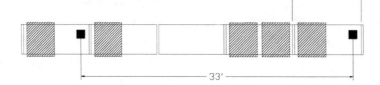

Figure 3.35. Trucks Versus Storage Modules

Storage Module	Storage Depth In No. of Units	Handling Equipment				
		Counter-balanced Lift Truck	Narrow Aisle		Very Narrow Aisle	
			Reach Lift Truck	Deep Reach Lift Truck	Very Narrow Aisle Lift Truck	AS/RS Stacker Crane
Floor Storage	Variable	X	O	O	—	—
Drive-in Racks	Variable	X	O	O	—	—
Push-Back Racks	Variable	X	X	X	X	O
Double Deep Racks	2	—	O	X	—	—
Selective Racks	1	X	X	X	X	X
Approximate Lift Height in Feet (Common Models)		20	30	30	40	100
Typical Storage Aisles in Feet		10.5–12	8–10	9–10	5–6.5	4.5–6

LEGEND: X : Intended for the module shown.
O : Workable; not intended for the module shown.
— : Not workable with module shown.

Step 2. Developing Space, Labor, and Equipment Requirements. Once the alternatives are defined and laid out to reflect the design criteria, the space, labor, and equipment requirements can be calculated for the projected design year.

Space Requirements. Space requirements can be calculated based on the following algorithm:

Storage Depth Per Pallet = Pallet Depth + Distance Between Pallets Within a Lane
(usually 3-inch clearance)

Storage Width Per Pallet = Floor Storage and Drive-in Racks: 54 Inches approx.

Pallet Racks: Pallet Width + Distance Between Lanes
(usually about 10 inches)

Space Per Pallet ={[(number of pallets in storage lanes x storage depth per pallet) + (0.5 x storage aisle width)] x [storage width per slot] x 1.2 (20% allowance for cross aisles)} ÷ {number of pallets in the storage lane x number of pallets in the vertical stack}.

For example: The space per pallet in double deep pallet racks with four levels of storage for 48-inch by 40-inch pallets and 10-feet wide storage aisles is calculated as follows:

{[(2 x 4.25 feet) + (0.5 x 10 feet)] x 4.17 feet x 1.2} ÷ {2 x 4} = 8.4 square feet per pallet

With a storage utilization allowance of 80%, the double deep pallet rack configuration will have an adjusted space per pallet of 10.5 square feet (8.4 square feet per pallet ÷ 0.80).

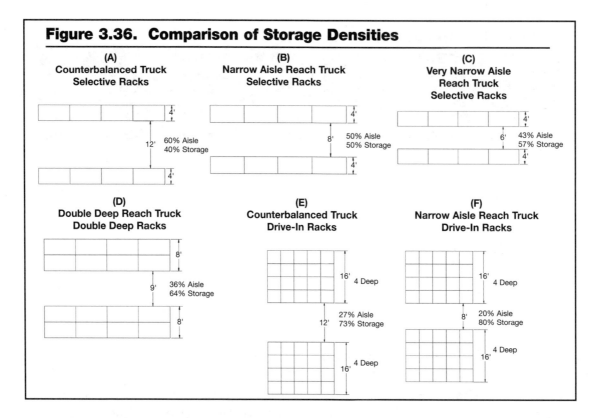

Figure 3.36. Comparison of Storage Densities

Figure 3.37 shows two examples of storage layout. **Figure 3.38** shows the results of different storage configurations based on these examples. Option 1 uses single deep pallet racks with four levels of storage. Option 2 uses five-deep bulk storage stacked two high with 12-foot aisles. Option 2a is the same as Option 2 except that pallets are stacked four high, thus cutting the square feet per pallet requirements in half.

The advent of computer-aided design, known as CAD, has decreased the time to design warehouses. Various CAD software on the market enables the designer to lay out different storage system combinations. In contrast to hand drafting, CAD saves tremendous amounts of time, especially when revisions have to be continually made to the drawing. To determine space requirements, the designer can use CAD to calculate the areas occupied by laying out storage alternatives.

Labor Requirements. The determination of labor requirements are a function of the throughput rate and the unit handling time. The unit handling time depends on the size of the facility, storage modules, and the handling equipment. The basic time elements involved in unit handling are:

- travel to pallet

- pick up the pallet or place it in staging area

- travel to or from the storage location

- move in and out of storage lane, if applicable

- store or retrieve pallet.

Figure 3.37. Pallet Storage Examples

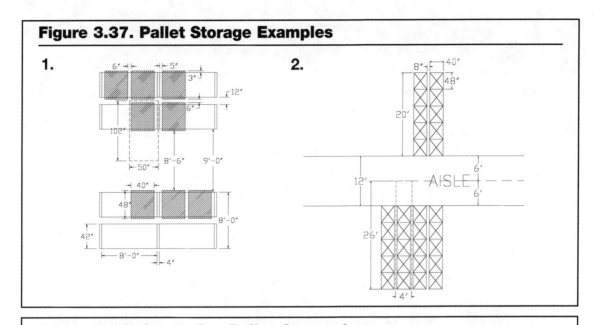

Figure 3.38. Space Per Pallet Comparison (from Figure 3.37)

	Unit of Measure	Option 1 Rack	Option 2 Bulk	Option 2a Rack
Pallet depth	inches	48	48	48
Pallet width	inches	40	40	40
Distance between lanes (side to side)	inches	10	8	8
Lane depth (number of pallets within a lane)	pallets	1	5	5
Distance between pallets within a lane (front to back)	inches	3	0	0
Stacking height	pallets	4	2	4
Aisle width	inches	102	144	144
Utilization (honeycombing factor)	percent	90%	65%	65%
Cross aisle overhead	percent	20%	20%	20%
Additional overhead (docks, offices, etc.)	percent	0%	0%	0%
Square feet/pallet		**11.8**	**19.2**	**9.6**

Time for pallet handling in staging, pallet storage, and retrieval will be almost the same for all alternatives. Travel distance to and from storage locations will vary depending on the total space for each alternative. Movement in and out of storage lanes will apply only to floor storage and drive-in rack alternatives. To estimate travel distance, it should be assumed that all pallets will be moved from outside the staging area to a single central location in the storage area. The simplest way of estimating this is to establish a square or rectangular storage block for each alternative based on the total storage space (total number of slots to be provided multiplied by the space per slot) and determine the approximate distance to a center point within that block.

To calculate the handling time per unit load, time values should be assigned to each element involved in the handling of a load. (See the previous chapter for more details.) These time values can be obtained from predetermined time standards or from actual time studies. A personal fatigue and delay (PF&D) factor should be added to each unit handling operation. To calculate the number of workers required, the daily throughput in number of pallets should be multiplied by the unit handling time and divided by the average minutes of work performed per day.

Equipment Requirements. This includes the number of storage modules, material handling equipment, storage medium (whether totes, corrugated boxes, skids, or pallets), and any other device that contributes to the storage function. The number of units of material handling equipment required can be calculated from the labor requirements with the assumption that one person will be assigned to one piece of handling equipment.

After the space, labor, and equipment requirements have been calculated for each storage alternative, the next step is to evaluate alternatives. Using costs as a basis for comparative analysis is discussed in the next chapter. Without involving costs or manpower values, the most efficient storage configuration on the basis of space is that plan which is able to store the required number of pallets in the least amount of space.

Figure 3.39. Design Year Inventory Profile

Pallet Range	Before Merger		Year 1: After Merger		Year 5: Design Year			
	No. of SKUs	Total Pallets[1]	No. of SKUs	Total Pallets[1]	No. of SKUs	Total Pallets[1]	% Total Pallets	Pallets/ SKU
Over 20	17	894	19	1,118	21	1,359	16.2%	64.7
11–20	40	732	44	915	48	1,113	13.2%	23.2
6–10	85	825	94	1,032	102	1,255	14.9%	12.3
1–5	589	2,009	648	2,512	702	3,054	36.3%	4.4
0.5–1	555	721	611	902	662	1,097	13.0%	1.7
.025–0.5	764	350	841	438	911	533	6.3%	0.6
0.05–0.25	2,152	366	2,368	458	2,564	[2] [3]	N/A	N/A
0–0.05	2,912	87	3,204	109	3,469	[2] [3]	N/A	N/A
Total	**7,114**	**5,984**	**7,829**	**7,484**	**8,479**	**8,411**		

For Year 1, the annual growth rate is 10% for the number of SKUs and 25% for the number of total pallets. For each year after that, the annual growth rate is 2% for the number of SKUs and 5% for the number of total pallets.

[1] Calculations were rounded up to the nearest pallet.

[2] These products to be stored in shelving.

[3] Some items to be stored in decked pallet racks.

A Working Example and Case Study[10]

Background. Mini Foods Inc., a retail operation, will merge with Major Foods, a larger competitor with four distribution centers. To service new stores introduced by the merger, Major Foods has decided to build a new facility adjacent to a refrigerated warehouse already owned by Mini Foods. Major Foods would like to take advantage of this new warehouse to alleviate a shortage of storage capacity in its other facilities. Major Foods also wants a warehouse to accommodate items not currently carried by Mini Foods. The merger has the following implications:

- Total number of SKUs and pallet volume for Mini Foods will increase by 10% and 25%, respectively, in the first year of the merger.

- After the merger, the number of SKUs and pallet volume will increase linearly by 2% and 5% per year, respectively. Forecasts are deemed reliable for 5 years.

- An average of 1,115 pallets will be handled each day in the design year.

Other assumptions are:

- SKUs requiring a cool room will be accommodated in the existing refrigerated warehouse. Dry SKUs will be stored in the new facility.

- The company will maintain an accurate inventory in pallet quantities.

The following steps were taken to build the model:

Step 1. Defining Objectives and Scope. Two main objectives were outlined for the study. The first one was to determine the amount of storage space required for the new facility. Major Foods also wanted to know the type of storage systems that would be best for the changing inventory profile. Refrigerated products were not included, as there was enough capacity in the refrigerated warehouse for both companies.

Step 2. Collecting, Organizing, and Profiling the Data. Pallet throughput per day was determined to be 1,115 pallets. Inventory data was collected and organized based on the peak inventory Mini Foods recorded the last year before the merger. **Figure 3.39** shows the inventory profile over three time periods: (a) before the merger; (b) after the merger, showing the growth in SKUs and pallet volume; and (c) during the design year, five years into the future. In Year 5, over 6,000 SKUs had less than one quarter of a pallet in inventory. These items were to be placed in shelving, preferably in the forward pick line, and eliminated from further storage analysis. A total of 8,411 full pallets would be stored.

Because the profile showed some SKUs averaged over 12 pallets per item, lanes that are 4 to 6 pallets deep were included in the analysis. Although expensive, management wanted to investigate the feasibility of push-back racks for items that had high throughput rates. Three of the four of Major Foods's facilities used a combination of selective and double deep racks. The fourth facility operated with selective racks in VNAs. Management's familiarity with these stor-

Figure 3.40. Generation of Storage Concepts

Concept No.	Type of Storage	No. of Pallets in Depth	No. of Pallets in Height	Handling Equipment Used	Approx. Clear Ceiling Height (Feet)
1	Floor	6	4	C. B. Lift Truck	20
2	Drive-in Racks	6	4	C. B. Lift Truck	20
3	Double Deep Racks	2	4	Deep Reach Lift Truck	20
4	Push-Back Racks	4	4	Reach Lift Truck	20
5	Push-Back Racks	2	4	Reach Lift Truck	20
6	Selective Racks	1	4	Reach Lift Truck	20
7	Selective Racks	1	10	Turret Truck (VNA)	50

Figure 3.41. Space Requirements

Concept No.	Type of Storage	No. of Pallets in Depth	No. of Pallets in Height	Depth of Storage Module (Feet)	Width of Storage Module (Feet)	Aisle Width (Feet)	Space Per Pallet (Sq. Ft.)
1	Floor	6	4	25.50	4.50	12	7.1
2	Drive-in Racks	6	4	25.00	4.50	12	7.0
3	Double Deep Racks	2	4	8.50	4.17	10	8.4
4	Push-Back Racks	4	4	17.00	4.17	9	6.7
5	Push-Back Racks	2	4	8.50	4.17	9	8.1
6	Selective Racks	1	4	4.25	4.17	9	10.9
7	Selective Racks	1	10	4.25	4.17	6	3.6

age systems made them candidate concepts for the new facility. **Figure 3.40** summarizes the different storage configurations.

Step 3. Developing Space and Handling Requirements. For each alternative, the space per pallet in square feet was calculated based on the space equation described previously. **Figure 3.41** summarizes the results. The VNA alternative had the lowest square feet per pallet. Handling requirements were calculated based on the expected throughput per day of 1,115 pallets (**Figure 3.42**). As turret trucks are slow in maneuvering outside of storage aisles, counterbalanced lift trucks were used to pick up and drop off pallets at the ends of the aisles (Alternative 7). This enabled the turret trucks to stay captive in the aisles for a more efficient operation.

Order Processing Space

The order processing area is where product, equipment, labor, and operating systems come together to accomplish the mission of the facility. Order processing includes all the elements required to assemble the correct quantity of each product or line item specified on an order in a form that is convenient for shipping. As in the storage area, the space required to accommodate this function in a warehouse varies significantly based on the requirements.

Before discussing the actual design process, one must first be acquainted with the different order processing components. They include:

• Order picking modules and equipment

• Order picking locations and strategies

• Order verification, packing, and consolidation.

Order Picking Modules and Equipment. Most storage modules described in the preceding section can be used as picking modules. In fact, storage areas of some warehouses incorporate the order-picking area where pickers pick full case quantities from the bottom levels of pallet racks in the storage area. With some degree of mechanization, pickers are able to pick from higher storage levels. Other pick modules are:

Shelving. This is the most popular and least expensive picking module. It also requires little or no maintenance. As a broken case pick module, shelving is used for slow-moving items with few picks per day. Inclined shelving incorporates shelves at an angle so that the carton openings face the picker. Although more expensive than regular shelving, this type of shelving promotes

Figure 3.42. Handling Requirements

Concept No.	Type of Storage	No. of Pallets in Depth	No. of Pallets in Height	Handling Equipment Used	Time Per Pallet (Minutes)	Pallets Per Day	Time Per Day (Minutes)	Equipment Required[1]
1	Floor	6	4	C. B. Lift Truck	3.2	1,115	3,568	8
2	Drive-in Racks	6	4	C. B. Lift Truck	3.3	1,115	3,680	9
3	Double Deep Racks	2	4	Deep Reach Lift Truck	3	1,115	3,345	8
4	Push-Back Racks	4	4	Reach Lift Truck	2.75	1,115	3,066	7
5	Push-Back Racks	2	4	Reach Lift Truck	2.75	1,115	3,066	7
6	Selective Racks	1	4	Reach Lift Truck	2.75	1,115	3,066	7
7	Selective Racks	1	10	Turret Truck (VNA)	2.4	1,115	2,676	6
				C. B. Lift Truck[2]	1.1	1,115	1,272	3

[1] Conversion to number of pieces of equipment and workers is based on a 7.5-hr. workday.

[2] Turret trucks are not very efficient when turning into cross aisles. Thus, counterbalanced trucks will be used for pick up and drop off of pallets at the end of the very narrow aisles.

Figure 3.43. Pick-to-Light Modules

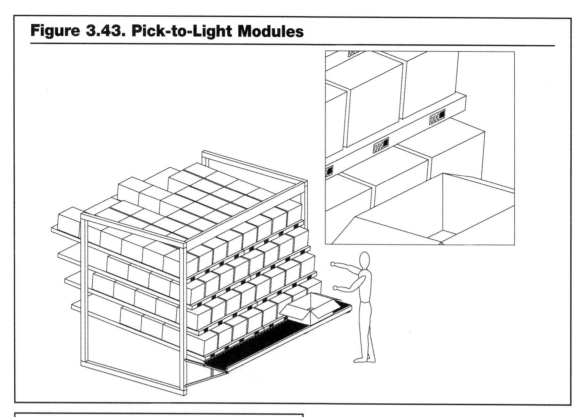

Figure 3.44. Picking From Pallet Flow Racks

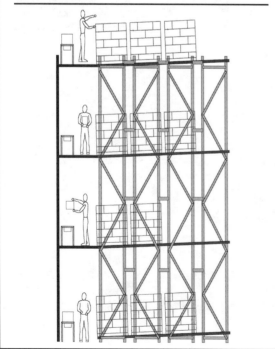

faster identification of the product and brings it closer to the worker.

Case Flow Racks. This type of picking module is common in a forward pick area. As a broken case pick module, flow racks are usually used for fast-moving items with multiple picks per day. Because of their depth, these racks can hold multiple cases and preserve FIFO product movement. As a full case pick module, flow racks are used for slower-moving items with few picks per day, but not so many that they have to be replenished more than every few days. For paperless picking applications, some flow racks have either light-emitting diodes (LED) or liquid crystal displays (LCD) on each lane and are called pick-to-light systems. (**Figure 3.43**.) There are many ways to implement pick-to-light systems. One method is to let the picker first scan the barcoded tote so that the computer can recognize the order. The computer then downloads the quantities to be picked to the LED or LCD panels in each lane or location. The picker picks the item and presses a button to verify that the pick was made.

Pallet Flow Racks. These racks are used primarily for full case picking and for products that require FIFO movement. As a broken case pick module, these racks are preferred for extremely fast-moving items. Pallet flow racks have depths of two or more pallets. **Figure 3.44** illustrates a four-level, four-pallet deep pick area where workers pick full cartons from pallet flow racks onto conveyors on each level.

Carousels. In the previously described picking modules, the picker goes to the product. Carousels bring the product to the picker, thus reducing the travel time to practically zero. In a vertical carousel, products rotate up and down instead of sideways (as in horizontal carousels), thus reducing the picking module's footprint. It is also used where security is a significant issue. To increase throughput, the picker can work with two or more carousels, also known as a "carousel pod." While the picker is picking from one carousel unit, an adjacent unit indexes and brings the next item to the pick station to save time. When the picker finishes his picks from the first unit, he turns to the next one. Pick-to-light technology is used where the picker is guided by a light tree that indicates which bin to pick from and how many pieces to pick. **Figure 3.45** illustrates this high-end pick-to-light horizontal carousel system.

Figure 3.45. Carousels with Pick-to-Light Technology

Light tree indicates the bin location and the number of pieces to be picked.

Multiple carousels form a pick pod for broken case picking.

Reprinted with permission from White Systems Inc., Kenilworth, NJ.

In addition to bringing product to the worker, carousels are relatively dense modules that can be stacked to optimize the cube of a building. They can also be fitted with automated load/extract mechanisms for a fully automated operation. The disadvantages are that they are expensive compared to static shelving, are less flexible in terms of capacity and application, and can be difficult to replenish.

Figure 3.46. A-Frame — Automated Order Selection Device

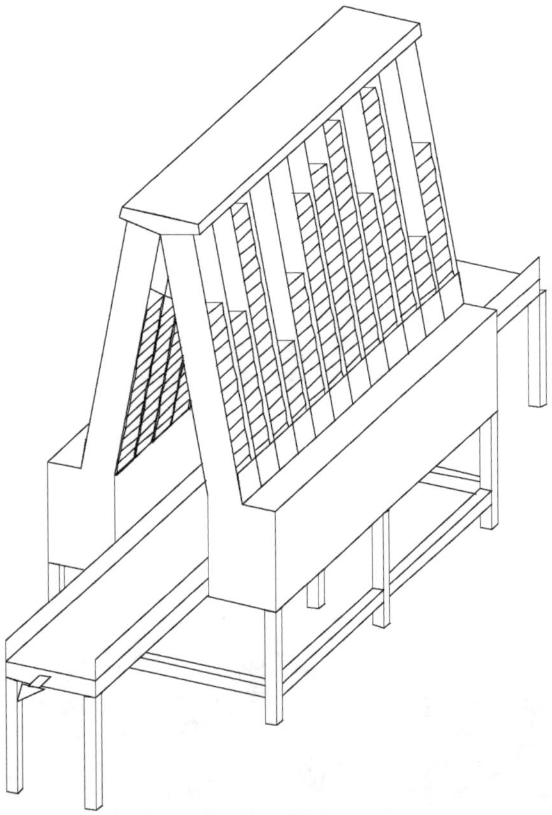

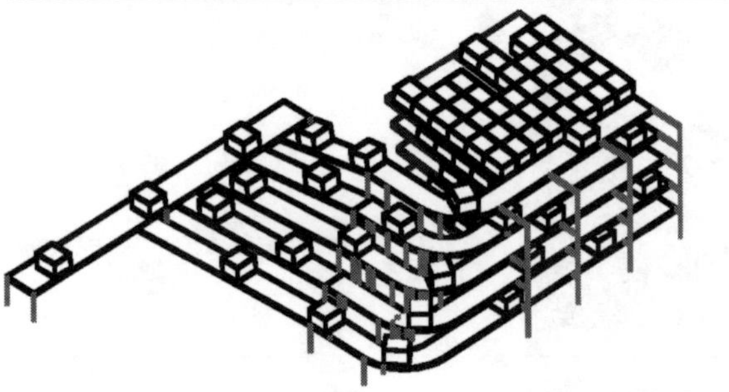

Automated Order Selection Systems. These systems allow orders to be processed quickly and accurately with no human intervention. Orders are downloaded to a host computer. Each SKU has its own lane, which has a trigger mechanism that releases the correct number of pieces or cases per line required in an order. The items released drop to a conveyor, where they are transported to a waiting tote for broken case items, or to a palletizer for full case items. For broken case picking, these selection devices can pick several lines per second. **Figure 3.46** shows one type of broken case selection system called an A-frame. Other systems are designed to pick a wider variety of product sizes and weight configurations within an enclosed storage unit for security. Full case selection systems have either computer-controlled trigger mechanisms that dispense the correct number of cases from specially designed flow racks on a conveyor, or use robotic arms to pick cases directly from a pallet to a conveyor or an automated guided vehicle (AGV). The cases are then transported to palletizing stations or directly into a waiting trailer. **Figure 3.47** is an example of a full case order selection system. In many of these systems, replenishment is expedited because each storage lane may update inventory in real time. When a lane is down to the last few pieces or cases, the computer will print a replenishment list

Figure 3.47. Automated Full Case Order Selection System

Figure 3.48. Electric Pallet Truck

Reprinted with permission from Crown Equipment Corporation, New Bremen, OH.

Figure 3.49. Orderpicker Truck

Reprinted with permission from Crown Equipment Corporation, New Bremen, OH.

or a light will signal the replenisher to restock the lane.

Equipment required to pick orders from the different picking modules include:

Carts. A cart is among the most inexpensive pieces of equipment used for picking orders. A picker can use a cart along rows of shelving or racks to pick multiple orders. The picker maintains order integrity by allotting different levels for each order or by placing dividers within each level. There are "smart" carts, which are equipped with a voice system or computer screen that tells the picker which item and the quantity to pick and in which order bin that product belongs. These carts are ergonomically designed to reduce worker fatigue.

Pallet Jacks. Pallet jacks are used to transport pallets horizontally. Some pallet jacks are equipped with a platform or step for the operator's convenience. Their use is usually confined to floor-level tasks. Some pallet jacks are manually pushed. Other jacks are electrically powered and are known as pallet trucks. Some pallet trucks may be used with the operator walking behind them and some may have a riding capability. **Figure 3.48** illustrates an electric pallet truck.

Orderpicker Trucks. Orderpicker trucks (**Figure 3.49**) work in 5-foot to 6-foot aisles. A platform attached to the mast enables the worker to pick to a pallet up to 30 feet high. In a full case picking system, slow-moving items would be on the higher levels of racks.

Conveyors. Conveyors are another means of transport between operations, floor levels, departments, and buildings. In the warehouse, where product is to be moved between specific points over a fixed path, where there is high cube density of SKUs, and where labor costs are high, the use of conveyors instead of lift trucks is better justified. Different kinds of conveyors exist for different applications. The type of conveyor is dependent on the following factors:

- Product characteristics

- Applications

- Other equipment that the conveyor works with

- Throughput or volume

- Speed.

Automated Storage and Retrieval Machines. Usually called a stacker crane, this machine retrieves full case and full pallet orders from storage modules. The order information is downloaded to the computer, which instructs the unmanned crane to retrieve the correct quantity of the correct items from the correct location and to transport it to a drop-off point.

Common warehouse conveyors

- Chutes. Chutes are often used for accumulation in shipping areas and to link two powered conveyors. Chutes are economical but may be difficult to control as the product is being conveyed.

- Flat Belt Conveyors. Flat belt conveyors are generally used for the transport of light- to medium-weight products between operations, floor levels, and departments. One advantage of a flat belt conveyor is its ability to transport through an incline or decline because of the friction between the load and the belt. This friction prevents the load or product from shifting or moving. For small and irregular loads, the belt may be supported by a slider bed; otherwise, it may be roller supported.

- Roller Conveyors. Roller conveyors are common and may either be powered or non-powered. Powered conveyors are usually driven by a chain or a belt. Roller conveyors are best suited for accumulation, merging, and sorting operations. The product to be transported should have a stiff bottom surface.

- Skate Wheel Conveyors. Skate wheel conveyors are generally limited to light-weight loads. Like roller conveyors, skate wheel conveyors are best suited for accumulation, merging, and sorting, but for light items.

- Chain Conveyors. Chain conveyors include one or more circular chains below the roller conveyor. A chain conveyor may be used to divert pallets or totes. The chains rise above the roller conveyor and make contact with the load, which may be diverted to another conveyor.

Order Picking Locations and Strategies. Picking can be done from one of two major locations: *picking from a forward picking area or picking directly from reserved storage.* Picking from a forward pick area increases productivity, as the pick path is reduced from the entire warehouse to a smaller, custom-designed pick area. However, it does require additional handling, as these forward pick locations have to be replenished depending on the capacity of the pick modules. The advantage of picking from the reserved area is that it usually results in increased space utilization, although it is not recommended for piece picking. Popular SKUs that show up on many orders benefit from a forward pick area for increased throughput, while slow-movers can be picked directly from reserved storage to conserve limited forward pick space. Where space is extremely critical, there may not be a forward picking area.

Order picking strategies can be categorized into three distinct types: (1) Single Order–Single Picker, (2) Zone Picking, and (3) Batch Picking.

Single Order–Single Picker. This type of picking strategy is used when one worker picks the entire order. In some instances, picking more than one order at a time may be done with a multilevel cart. **Figure 3.50** is a schematic diagram of the single order–single picker method.

Zone Picking. Zone picking involves several pickers. Part of the order is picked from one zone by one picker. Additional picks are worked on by other pickers in other zones. If the zones are not sequential, partial orders picked from the different zones will have to be consolidated, or "married." Zone picking is beneficial for orders with a large number of lines. A line is each unique item or stockkeeping unit that appears on an order. Sequential zone picking is advantageous when you have to process large numbers of orders and lines per order and when there is not enough space to consolidate an order. **Figure 3.51** shows a schematic diagram illustrating zone picking.

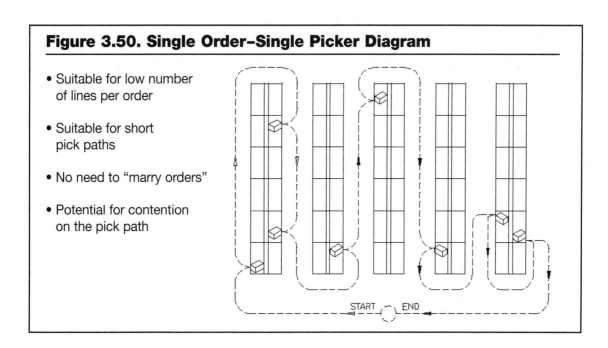

Figure 3.50. Single Order–Single Picker Diagram

- Suitable for low number of lines per order

- Suitable for short pick paths

- No need to "marry orders"

- Potential for contention on the pick path

START   END

Figure 3.51. Zone Pick Diagram

- Suitable for orders with high line count

- Reduces travel time

- Requires consolidation

- Reduces bottlenecks

Batch Picking. Batch picking involves grouping the same items of a group of orders. One or more unit loads of items for this group of orders are laid out in a forward picking area, where a picker assembles each order (**Figure 3.52**). The batch picking concept reduces unnecessary travel time by consolidating the items into a smaller area for later picking. This type of picking is particularly useful when there are many items in inventory but the same few items are on many orders (e.g., for distributors whose customers are retail store chains).

Figure 3.52. Batch Pick Diagram

- Suitable for many SKUs in inventory with a low pick density

- Reduces travel time

- Requires forward pick or consolidation

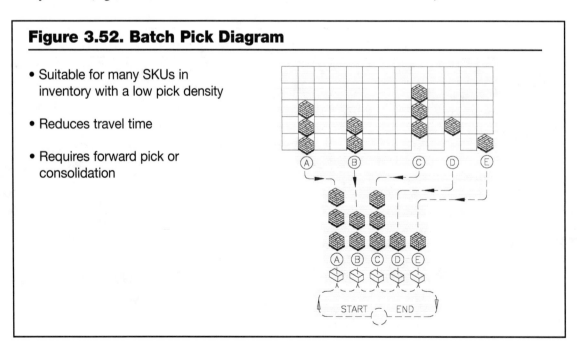

Order Verification, Packing, and Consolidation. When the order has been completely picked, it is transported to a staging area for order verification. Verification is the process of checking the orders. Any discrepancy causes the order to be diverted to a holding area for correction. A manual verification system has workers who visually check products against picking tickets or invoices. Some barcode verification systems have workers scanning the shipping box to download the order number. Then the computer verifies that the correct item has been picked as each item is scanned. This type of verification can be implemented as the product is picked, thus eliminating double handling. With picking and verification done concurrently, the order can proceed directly to the packing stations. Manual packing stations have been ergonomically designed so that the packing materials and the product are all within reach of the worker. There are a number of automated packing stations that are designed for virtually any packing configuration. Consolidation involves sorting the cases that are part of a larger order. For full case orders, each case may have to be labeled and sent either to palletizers or directly to trailers, where the cartons are hand stacked.

Developing Design Requirements. The successful design of an effective order processing system begins with an in-depth analysis of the company's order characteristics, order profiles, and movement data by item. This historical data can then be used as the basis to determine design year requirements. The key is to design for flexibility. Depending on resources, some companies design for peak movement estimates. Others design for average movement and add manpower during the peak season. Start with a relatively manual operation. As space and throughput requirements strain that design, the use of technology should be considered, such as adding pick-to-light, carousels, or mezzanines to improve capacity and throughput.

The steps for designing the order processing area include:

1. Collecting product data, movement data, order characteristics, and other design parameters

2. Organizing and profiling the data

3. Adjusting and projecting for design year requirements.

Step 1. Collecting Product Data, Movement Data, Order Characteristics, and Other Design Parameters. The information required for designing the order processing area may already be on file from the design of the storage area. It can also be used for a more detailed slotting of each SKU. In this section, the focus is on the overall design of order processing space and how it impacts a warehouse's space requirements. For more information on slotting, refer to the bibliography at the end of this book.[11]

Product Data. For each SKU, the following product information would be required:

• Item number

• Description

- Special storage requirements (i.e., refrigerated, hazardous, etc.)

- Dimensions (L, W, H)

- Unit cube

- Weight

- Units per carton

- Cartons per pallet

- Other special requirements, such as specific temperature controls, stackability if the product is irregularly shaped, or special handling equipment that is required.

This information should be accessible from an SKU master file. Many companies do not maintain records of SKU dimensions or cube, which are critical for the proper design of the order processing area. The size of a pick module can be affected if a three-foot wide carton is slotted for a two-foot wide facing. For companies whose carton sizes are routinely undergoing changes in dimensions or are constantly receiving new items, it may be advantageous to use an instrument that scans and records carton dimensions and weight.

Slotting

Slotting is the process of assigning products to an appropriate storage or picking location by taking into account the factors that influence the movement, staging, and storage of the SKU in the warehouse. It determines for each SKU:

- An appropriate storage and picking module

- An appropriate allocation of space in the module

- The module's location within the warehouse

- The exact location within the module.

The slotting process progressively consolidates items into groups with similar characteristics based on specific user rules to maximize picking productivity.

Movement Data. This information, preferably cubic movement, for each SKU is another useful set of statistics to be collected to determine the type, size, and placement of a pick module.

Order Characteristics. Customer order history for each order should indicate customer identification number, unique SKUs requested on the order and the quantities of each (also known as a line item on an order), order date, and method of shipment (whether USPS, tractor-trailer, or any independent carriers, such as UPS and FedEx). A 12-month sample will be necessary for highly seasonal businesses. However, if demand and SKU movement do not vary over the year, then a smaller sample would be sufficient. A typical set of orders can be analyzed and used as a basis for projections. Statistics collected from the order profile include line items per order, units per order, units per line item, total weight per order, and number of orders to process each day.

Other Design Parameters. Other pertinent information related to order processing is required. Business projections such as increasing the number of SKUs, changing packaging configurations, and adding new stores all directly affect the space requirements of the order processing area. For forward picking systems, the rate of replenishment should be determined.

Replenishment is time consuming and labor intensive. The fewer the replenishments, the larger the pick module space required by an SKU. Replenishing a pick location once a week means that the pick location must have the capacity for at least one week's average volume.

Step 2. Organizing and Profiling the Data. The first step involves a preliminary grouping of SKUs based on their storage requirements. Flammable items are grouped together, since OSHA rules dictate separate storage and pick areas for them. Cool rooms may be required for certain items under strict temperature control. High-value products may require a secure pick location with limited access. For each grouping, SKUs are further organized based on the order unit quantity. A picking system will vary greatly depending upon the unit quantity of the products ordered — whether in broken case or piece-pick quantities, full case, full pallet, or a combination. There are four general types: (1) Full pallet picking, (2) Full case picking, (3) Broken case picking, and (4) Awkward or hard-to-handle item picking. Full pallet picking entails retrieving items in minimum full pallet quantities. For full case picking, the picker picks products in minimum full case quantities. Broken case picking consists of breaking up a case quantity of an item and picking in piece quantities. Awkward or hard-to-handle items are generally picked separately from the other types because of the handling difficulty.

Some of the statistics to be determined for each SKU include:

SKU Popularity. This is sometimes referred to as "number of hits" or number of picks for an SKU. For the picker, this translates into the number of times he travels to a location to pick a given SKU. On a set of customer order forms, it would be the number of times an SKU appears.

Demand for the SKU. This information is the total quantity of an SKU shipped during the period of the study.

Unit Cube of the Item. This is the physical size of an SKU. It may be in the form of a carton, tote, piece, or a pallet load. Its cube is determined by multiplying its length, width, and height. Another method for determining SKU cube would be to determine the cube of an outer container divided by the number of units in the container.

Cube Movement. The demand in SKUs multiplied by the unit cube for each equals the cube movement for the period. Picking rules for an SKU that moves 50 units for a given period varies greatly depending on the unit size — an SKU that is as small as a paper clip requires a different approach than an SKU as big as a refrigerator.

Profiling determines trends so that decisions can be made for groups of SKUs with similar cube movement, pick density, etc. These charts include the following:

Movement Profiles. This analysis groups SKUs according to a specified movement range. **Figure 3.53** illustrates a sample movement profile of a full case pick operation. Where applicable, the cube movement should be used in the analysis. SKUs that ship less than 0.1 cubic foot per month could be slotted for bin shelving. Conversely, SKUs with movement of over 1,500 cubic feet per month could be picked directly from pallet flow racks.

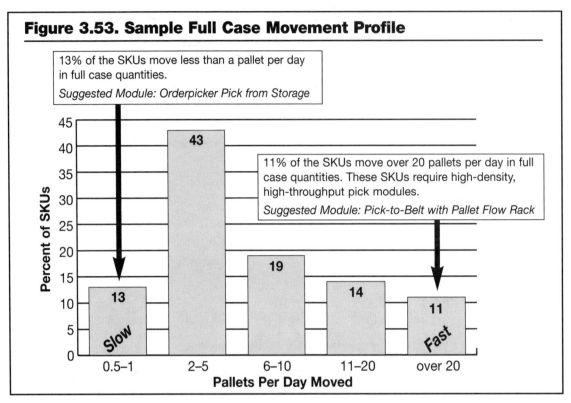

Figure 3.53. Sample Full Case Movement Profile

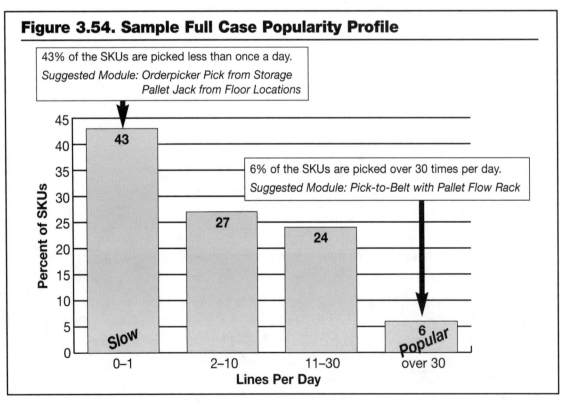

Figure 3.54. Sample Full Case Popularity Profile

Popularity Profiles (**Figure 3.54**). This analysis indicates the percentage of SKUs that historically have the most picks by measuring the number of times each SKU appears as a line item in an order for a specific time period. For full pallet picking, most frequently picked SKUs should be picked from pallet flow racks, drive-in racks, or bulk storage closest to the docks. In full case, high-volume picking, picking to conveyors from pallet flow racks may be the solution. Broken case picking systems should pick slow movers from shelving and fast movers from multiple carousel pods or case flow racks. Again, these applicable picking modules are dependent on the load size. As opposed to pallet racks, case flow racks and shelving have significant size and weight limitations.

Step 3. Adjusting and Projecting for Design Year Requirements. Projecting the above historical data to design year requirements will require sales and business forecasts. How many SKUs will be added? How much volume is anticipated from the sale of these additional SKUs? All of these have to be taken into account to determine design year requirements.

Generating Alternative Picking Designs. This section can be divided into two major steps:

1. Developing general picking concepts and layouts.

2. Developing space, labor, and equipment requirements.

Step 1. Developing General Picking Concepts and Layouts. By looking at the profiles, determine how each group of SKUs will be picked. **Figure 3.55** compares the different picking alternatives and their applicability. The assignment of products to these modules must satisfy

Figure 3.55. Various Picking Configurations

	Pick-to-Cart	Batch Pick-to-Tote	Horizontal Carousel	Vertical Carousel	Pick-to-Belt	Powered Pallet Jack	Man-Up Orderpicker Truck	Automated Order Picker	Mini-Load System
Type of Picking	Piece Pick	Piece Pick	Piece Pick	Piece Pick	Full Case	Full Case	Full Case	Piece Pick Full Case	Piece Pick Full Case
Hourly Throughput	30–100 lines	100–250 lines	25–300 lines	25–400 lines	200–400 cases	30–80 lines	20–60 lines	approx. 900 orders	25–100 lines
Suggested Pick Modules	Shelving Case Flow Rack	Shelving Case Flow Rack	n/a	n/a	Pallet Flow Rack Pallet Rack Bulk Pallet	Pallet Flow Rack Pallet Rack Bulk Pallet	Pallet Rack Bulk Pallet	Custom	Custom
Item Security	Low	Low	Medium	High	Low	Low	Medium	High	High
Maintenance	Low	Low	Medium	Medium	Medium	Low	Medium	High	High
Flexibility	High	High	Medium	Medium	Medium	High	High	Low	Low

Throughput is highly variable and depends on layout, controls, level of information systems technology, peripheral equipment such as pick-to-light, and locator systems.

Figure 3.56. Order Picking Alternatives

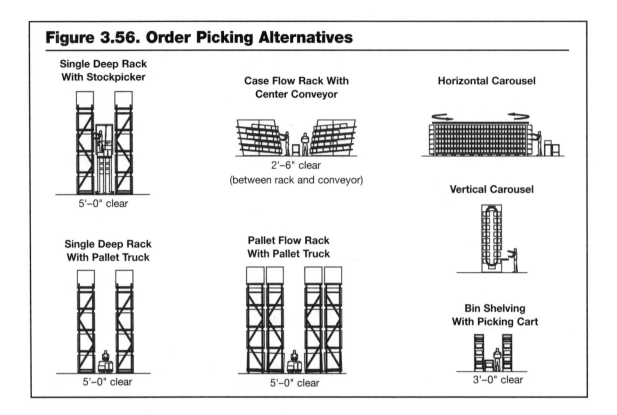

Single Deep Rack With Stockpicker
5'-0" clear

Case Flow Rack With Center Conveyor
2'-6" clear
(between rack and conveyor)

Horizontal Carousel

Vertical Carousel

Single Deep Rack With Pallet Truck
5'-0" clear

Pallet Flow Rack With Pallet Truck
5'-0" clear

Bin Shelving With Picking Cart
3'-0" clear

the throughput requirements, maximize space utilization, and ensure sufficient control and security of material, but still be cost justified. **Figure 3.56** illustrates order picking alternatives. Aisle clearances may change depending on the type of equipment. A large cart may not be suitable for aisles of 3-foot clear within bin shelving.

Step 2. Developing Space, Labor, and Equipment Requirements. Space requirements will depend on the size of the pick modules. Unlike pallet racks that come in fairly standard sizes, pick modules are more customized and can vary in size. **Figure 3.57** lists common shelving and case flow rack sizes, the units they can store, and the number of facings or unique positions they contain based on 12-inch x 12-inch x 12-inch cartons. The total number of pick modules required will be based on the number of SKUs, the number of positions dedicated to each SKU, and the number of facings available on a pick module.

For example, consider a piece-pick operation where 180 of the most popular SKUs are to be picked to totes from case flow racks as shown in **Figure 3.58**. Each case flow rack module is 5-feet wide by 10-feet deep with a capacity for 20 facings. To reduce replenishment, 20 of the SKUs will occupy double facings in the case flow rack, for a total of 200 facings required (180 single facings + 20 additional facings for the high-volume SKUs). Thus, the number of case flow rack modules required will be 10 (200 ÷ 20). To determine space requirements, the total depth of a module must first be calculated, including allowances for aisles and conveyors. For this example, the total depth of a module can be calculated as follows:

Depth of one case flow rack module =	10 feet
Half of a 10-foot replenishment aisle =	5 feet
Picker aisle =	3 feet
Roller conveyor width =	2 feet
Half of the powered takeaway conveyor =	1 foot
Total depth of module:	21 feet

With a width of 5 feet, each case flow rack module has an area footprint of 105 sq. ft. (5 feet x 21 feet). For 10 modules, the total area required by this piece-pick operation is 1,050 sq. ft. The use of CAD facilitates the calculation of space requirements for picking. With CAD, one can lay out the different picking configurations and use the program to determine the space requirements for each area.

Labor and equipment requirements are best determined from a time study of the pick operation. (See Chapter 2.) Where the proposed pick operation is similar to an existing one, past productivity can be used to determine future requirements. For example, an existing operation

Figure 3.57. Facings and Storage Capacity Of Common Pick Modules

Storage Module (Based on 12" x 12" x 12" case cube)	Type of Units Stored	Dimensions in Inches			No. of Facings	No. of Units Stored
		Width	Depth	Height		
Case Flow Racks Bay	Cases	60	120	96	20	200
Static Shelving Bay	Cases	36	24	84	15	30
Heavy-Duty Shelving Bay	Cases	96	24	84	48	96

Dimensions indicated are clear bay dimensions and do not include upright and frame widths.

Figure 3.58. Piece-Pick, Pick-to-Tote Example With Case Flow Racks

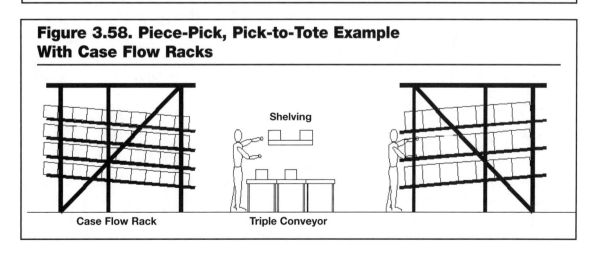

Case Flow Rack   Triple Conveyor

of 10 pickers in a pick-to-belt operation can process 3,000 cartons per hour (or 300 cartons per picker). If the proposed system is expected to handle 4,500 cartons per hour, a total of 15 pickers would be required (4,500 cartons ÷ 300 cartons/picker) for the future.

A Last Word on Space

The planning and design of the receiving, shipping, storage, and order processing spaces of a warehouse can be daunting. With so many products, strategies, and possible equipment configurations, it is easy to lose focus and incorrectly estimate space requirements. A systematic approach "covering all the bases" of warehousing must be adopted. Throughout the planning process, keep in mind the primary goals of the warehouse — whether it is maximizing the utilization of space and/or optimizing throughput. The following design tips will help warehouse managers achieve both:

- Consider cross docking. Move full pallets from receiving, directly to shipping. This will reduce storage space as inventory is eliminated.

- Consider a detailed slotting of products into the pick modules with ergonomic principles in mind.

- Use advanced technology such as pick-to-light, voice systems, and radio frequency devices.

- Use mezzanines to improve cubic utilization and reduce space requirements.

- Put shelving over conveyors.

- Put pallet racks behind case flow racks for quick replenishment of popular items.

- Use the floor location of the reserved storage area as pick locations when a forward picking area is not possible.

- Perhaps the most important design tip is to always allow for expansion in the design. Dynamic business conditions and changing customer requirements make designing for flexibility a necessity.

Chapter 4
WAREHOUSE COST CALCULATIONS

The financial aspects of warehousing are a major concern to warehouse managers. Aside from keeping track of costs that are incurred in day-to-day operations, the manager must generate strategies to reduce these costs. Whether improving an existing warehouse or designing a new one, choosing the best strategy entails using cost calculations to aid in decision making.

We can categorize costs into two major areas: the capital costs and the operating costs. Capital costs are the one-time costs involved in design, construction, implementation, and start-up of a new or improved warehouse. Operating costs are the day-to-day expenses in the actual running of a warehouse after start-up. The costs illustrated in this chapter are current costs of materials and labor at the time of publication. These costs are a guide; actual costs may vary considerably from those listed. They do not include freight and taxes or special conditions. For instance, racks in states with seismic requirements would be more expensive.

In justifying a warehouse design project, costs take on great significance. They become the crux by which management decides whether or not to implement a proposed design. By identifying appropriate costs and properly allocating them, savings can be calculated and used to justify capital expenditures. Our focus will be on the immediate, measurable savings. These include reduction in labor (salaries, benefits, and other costs), equipment, operating expenses, and inventory. Other benefits, such as increased sales and customer satisfaction due to fewer errors and faster response, are harder to measure and contribute more to the long term. Refer to the bibliography at the end of the book for more discussion on quantifying these costs.

Capital Costs

The capital costs of an investment are the costs from the planning and design; purchase, delivery, and installation of equipment; facility construction or renovation; and other peripheral costs associated with a new design. Managers have to examine alternatives in making decisions concerning new building layouts, operating system changes, and new equipment purchases. To compare alternatives, capital costs are required to justify the project and determine the most feasible design. The following steps are required to determine the total capital costs of a warehouse design project:

1. Identify building/construction costs.

2. Identify material handling equipment costs.

3. Identify storage equipment costs.

4. Determine and identify other special costs. These include planning and design, information systems, and other peripheral costs.

Step 1. Identify Building/Construction Costs. Some designs may require simple changes to the warehouse, such as adding a dock door, removal of walls, or shifting pallet racks. Capacity requirements may force the building of a new facility. **Figure 4.1** shows the latest collection of nationwide averages of material, installation, and construction costs per square foot of floor area compiled by R. S. Means, a publishing and consulting firm specializing in construction. These costs were calculated using basic construction specifications for a warehouse with no conveyors or elevators. They do not include costs for site work, such as roads, parking, and site improvements. A 15% factor has been added for overhead and profit, plus an additional 7% for architect's fees.

There are many factors that affect construction costs. The more important ones include:

Ceiling Height. Many conventional warehouses have a clear height of 24 feet to 30 feet.

Figure 4.1. Typical Building/Construction Costs

Exterior Wall	Area (square feet)	10,000	15,000	20,000	25,000	30,000	35,000	40,000	50,000	60,000
	Perimeter (linear feet)	410	500	600	700	700	766	833	966	1,000
		Cost ($)								
Brick with concrete block back-up	Steel frame	87.30	78.50	74.55	72.15	67.70	66.10	65.00	63.35	60.80
	Bearing walls	85.80	76.85	72.75	70.30	65.75	64.15	63.00	61.30	58.75
Concrete block	Steel frame	71.40	65.50	62.80	61.20	58.55	57.50	56.75	55.75	54.25
	Bearing walls	69.60	63.65	60.90	59.25	56.55	55.55	54.75	53.70	52.20
Galvanized steel siding	Steel frame	75.00	68.95	66.20	64.55	61.80	60.80	60.00	58.95	57.40
Metal sandwich panels	Steel frame	75.85	69.15	66.05	64.25	61.10	59.90	59.05	57.85	56.05
Perimeter adjustment, add or deduct	Per 100 linear feet	8.70	5.75	4.35	3.45	2.90	2.45	2.15	1.75	1.45
Story height adjustment, add or deduct	Per 1 foot	1.20	0.95	0.90	0.80	0.70	0.65	0.60	0.60	0.50

For basement, add $17.65 per square foot of basement area.

Source: Means *Square Foot Costs 2002*. Copyright R. S. Means Co. Inc., Kingston, MA. All rights reserved.

However, there are increased benefits and added costs in buildings with clear heights of 32 to 50 feet. For automated storage and retrieval systems, storage racks can extend to a height of over 100 feet. Substantial savings can be anticipated if the rack structure supports the roof and walls.

Location. Costs of materials and labor vary from state to state. **Figure 4.2** shows the different location factors by state to be multiplied to the nationwide average costs in **Figure 4.1** to achieve a more accurate local cost estimate. The physical characteristics of the site affect building costs. The site may have to be graded for proper drainage. The stability and weight-bearing

Figure 4.2. Location Factors

States and Possessions	Location Factor	States and Possessions	Location Factor	States and Possessions	Location Factor
Alabama	0.79	Kansas	0.82	North Carolina	0.73
Alaska	1.25	Kentucky	0.85	North Dakota	0.83
Arizona	0.86	Louisiana	0.82	Ohio	0.96
Arkansas	0.75	Maine	0.89	Oklahoma	0.80
California	1.10	Maryland	0.86	Oregon	1.03
Colorado	0.90	Massachusetts	1.06	Pennsylvania	0.98
Connecticut	1.05	Michigan	0.96	Rhode Island	1.04
District of Columbia	0.95	Minnesota	0.99	South Carolina	0.74
Delaware	1.01	Mississippi	0.72	South Dakota	0.78
Florida	0.82	Missouri	0.93	Tennessee	0.78
Georgia	0.78	Montana	0.89	Texas	0.78
Guam	1.33	Nebraska	0.79	Utah	0.87
Hawaii	1.23	Nevada	0.98	Vermont	0.77
Idaho	0.89	New Hampshire	0.87	Virginia	0.80
Illinois	1.02	New Jersey	1.09	Washington	1.01
Indiana	0.93	New Mexico	0.89	West Virginia	0.91
Iowa	0.84	New York	1.13	Wisconsin	0.96
				Wyoming	0.78

Canadian (Reflects Canadian Currency)

Alberta	0.95	New Foundland	0.94	Quebec	1.01
British Columbia	1.05	Nova Scotia	0.95	Saskatchewan	0.91
Manitoba	0.96	Ontario	1.06		
New Brunswick	0.92	Prince Edward Island	0.90		

Note: Average location factor by state derived from local location factors in Means *Square Foot Costs 2002*. Copyright R. S. Means Co. Inc., Kingston, MA. All rights reserved.

qualities of the soil must be determined. Additional costs are incurred in checking soil conditions, securing various permits, etc.

Building Configuration and Size. The recommended ratio of land to initial building in industrial sites or zones is 3 to 1. The 3:1 ratio includes allowances for a truck yard, off-street car parking, and 100 percent building expansion. Generally, not more than one half of the site can be built upon, which can limit future expansion. Initial construction should provide operating space adequate for at least five years after building. The size and shape of the site will influence the building size and configuration. The warehouse may have to be designed to fit an odd shape to maximize the use of available space. The most economical construction is a square building, since it has the least amount of perimeter wall. From an operations perspective, this configuration may be inefficient because of excessive travel distances between major traffic areas. If the warehouse will be outgrown in 10 to 15 years and be put up for sale, the building should not be too highly specialized to make it flexible for others to use.

Bay Size. As was previously discussed, the distance between columns should be compatible with an efficient layout. With fewer columns, there is more flexibility. However, as column bay sizes increase, structural costs may also increase. Developers like to have standard bay sizes to save on engineering costs. Due to seismic and weather requirements, some areas have a maximum limit on column spacings. Local building codes should be checked for bay size limits.

Floors. A sound, level floor, free of cracks, is important. High-traffic areas, such as shipping, should use a surface hardener to reduce wear. Very narrow aisle systems require superflat floors. These requirements will increase the overall construction costs.

Walls. Masonry walls of brick, block, or tilt-up concrete are durable and require low maintenance. However, insulation may not be adequate, especially in cold climates. If metal siding is used, a masonry wall at least six feet high above the floor is recommended to avoid damage from lift trucks. Any effort to enhance the aesthetic appearance also increases costs.

Insulation and Temperature Controls. Warehouses requiring refrigeration increase construction costs markedly. Energy costs can be reduced with more insulation in walls and ceilings. Under the Building Officials and Code Administrators International Inc. (BOCA) National Building Code, a heated warehouse must be insulated to conserve energy.

Step 2. Identify Material Handling Equipment Costs. Material handling costs vary with the type of equipment. **Figure 4.3** shows typical cost estimates for various material handling equipment. For stacker cranes, costs are usually quoted as part of a total system because of their specific applications. For lift trucks, costs are a function of load capacity, maximum lift height, duty cycles per hour, operating aisle width, and normal operating hours. For conveyors, costs are a function of the type of conveyor, linear feet required, and complexity of controls, including the number of turns, sorts, and merges. **Figure 4.4** estimates the project cost breakdown for conveyor systems in complex systems integration projects. Forty percent of the cost is attributed to the mechanical hardware, which includes the actual conveyors and supports.

Figure 4.3. Material Handling Equipment Costs

Electric Trucks (w/Battery and Charger):	Lower Range	Upper Range
Walkie Pallet Jack (4,000# Cap.)	$4,500	$5,500
Walkie Pallet Jack (6,000# Cap.)	$6,500	$8,500
Rider Pallet Jack (6,000# Cap.)	$7,500	$9,500
Rider Pallet Jack (8,000# Cap.)	$10,000	$11,500
Rider Pallet Jack (Tandem 6,000# Cap.)	$7,900	$11,000
Rider Pallet Jack (Tandem 8,000# Cap.)	$8,500	$12,500
Manually Propelled Straddle Stacker (1,500–2,000# Cap./Light-Duty Walk-Behind)	$2,500	$4,000
Self-Propelled Straddle Stacker (2,000# Cap./Light-Duty Walk-Behind)	$6,000	$8,000
Self-Propelled Straddle Stacker (3,000# Cap./Heavy-Duty Walk-Behind)	$12,000	$14,000
Self-Propelled Straddle Stacker (4,000# Cap./Heavy-Duty Walk-Behind)	$13,000	$15,000
Walkie/Reach Truck (3,000# Cap. Walk Behind)	$16,000	$18,000
Hydraulic Maintenance Lifts (Manually Propelled Elevating Platforms)	$5,000	$12,000
Order Selector Truck (3,000# Cap.) (w/Wire Guidance Add $5,000)	$19,000	$25,000
Low-Level Order Selector Truck (Up to 2,000# Cap.)	$10,000	$13,000
Counterbalanced Truck (3,000# Three-Wheel)	$21,000	$24,000
Counterbalanced Truck (4,000# Three- or Four-Wheel)	$24,000	$26,000
Counterbalanced Truck (5,000# Four-Wheel)	$26,000	$28,000
Counterbalanced Truck (6,000# Four-Wheel)	$28,000	$32,000
Narrow Aisle Reach Truck (3,000# Cap.)	$23,000	$30,000
Narrow Aisle Reach Truck (4,000# Cap.)	$25,000	$32,000
Narrow Aisle Reach Truck (4,500# Cap.)	$28,000	$35,000
Double Deep Reach Truck (2,500# Cap.)	$26,000	$34,000
Double Deep Reach Truck (3,000# Cap.)	$26,000	$34,000
Turret Truck (Man-Up)	$65,000	$95,000
Turret Truck (Man-Down)	$50,000	$75,000
Swing Mast Truck	$60,000	$80,000
Narrow Aisle Articulating	$45,000	$65,000
Guidance Systems:	Lower Range	Upper Range
For use in very narrow aisles w/turret trucks and order pickers		
Wire Guidance	$3	$5
Rail Guidance	$12	$17
Battery Changing/Charging Systems:	Lower Range	Upper Range
Electro-Magnetic Battery Changing/Charging System Base Price (Plus Costs Listed Below)	$18,000	$37,000
Add this cost for each battery position in the system	$450	$850
Propane Trucks:	Lower Range	Upper Range
Counterbalanced Truck (3,000# Cap.)	$15,000	$18,000
Counterbalanced Truck (4,000# Cap.)	$17,000	$20,000
Counterbalanced Truck (5,000# Cap.)	$19,000	$22,000
Counterbalanced Truck (6,000# Cap.)	$21,000	$24,000

Figure 4.3. Material Handling Equipment Costs (continued)

Manual Pallet Trucks (Pallet Jacks):	Lower Range	Upper Range
(48" L x 27" W)		
Standard Steel	$500	$900
Zinc Plated (For Corrosive/Wet-Down)	$800	$1,200
Stainless Steel (For FDA/USDA)	$2,000	$3,000

Lift Truck Options:	Lower Range	Upper Range
Carton Clamp	$7,000	$9,000
Paper Roll Clamp	$8,000	$10,000
Slip Sheet-Push/Pull	$6,000	$8,000
Side-Shifter	$1,200	$2,000
Drum Handler (Single Non-Hydraulic)	$1,200	$1,800
Drum Handler (Double Non-Hydraulic)	$2,400	$3,600
Drum Handler (Single Hydraulic)	$5,500	$7,500
Drum Handler (Double Hydraulic)	$7,000	$9,500

Automatic Guided Vehicles (AGVs):	Lower Range	Upper Range
AGV Unit-Load Carrier with Roller Deck (Includes AGV Controller, Wireless or Wired Path, Batteries, Chargers, etc.)	$200,000	$250,000
AGV Tow Vehicle (Includes AGV Controller, Wireless or Wired Path, Batteries, Chargers, etc.)	$150,000	$200,000
AGV Tow Trailer Without Roller Bed	$3,000	$5,000
AGV Tow Trailer With Non-Powered Roller Bed	$12,000	$16,000
AGV Tow Trailer With Powered Roller Bed	$20,000	$25,000
AGV Pick-Up & Delivery (P&D) Stations	$9,000	$15,000

Conveyor:	Lower Range	Upper Range
Powered Roller (Per Linear Foot)	$200	$275
Zero Pressure Accumulation (Per Linear Foot)	$250	$350
Belt (Per Linear Foot)	$180	$250
Trash (Per Linear Foot)	$250	$300
Gravity Roller/Skate (Per Linear Foot)	$25	$50
Flexible Skate Wheel (Per Linear Foot Extended) (Collapsed Length is Approximately 1/4 of Extended)	$75	$125

Sorters (Cartons):		
Pop-up Wheel Sorter	$300 per foot + $5,000 per divert	
Pusher Sorter	$300 per foot + $4,500 per divert	
Shoe Sorter	$2,000 per foot + $5,000 per divert	

Sorters (Unit):	Lower Range	Upper Range
Cross-Belt Sorter (Per Linear Foot)	$4,000	$5,000
Tilt-Tray Sorter (Per Linear Foot)	$4,500	$5,000

Figure 4.3. Material Handling Equipment Costs (continued)

Induction/Output (For above Sorters):	Lower Range	Upper Range
Induction Points for Cross-Belt or Tilt Tray (Each) (Minimum of One Induction Point Per System)	$25,000	$50,000
Sort Chutes (Per Destination)	$10,000	$20,000

Accumulator, Metering Belt, Induction Belt, Scanners:	Lower Range	Upper Range
Needed for all types of sortation systems		
Low Speed (40–60 Cartons per minute)	$40,000	$60,000
Medium Speed (70–90 Cartons per minute)	$50,000	$70,000
High Speed (100–120 Cartons per minute)	$80,000	$100,000

Sortation Control System and PLCs (Programmed Logic Controllers):	Lower Range	Upper Range
Needed for all types of sortation systems		
Low Complexity	$40,000	$60,000
Medium Complexity	$60,000	$100,000
High Complexity	$100,000	$250,000

Miscellaneous Handling Equipment:	Lower Range	Upper Range
Chain Hoists (1/4 HP/500 lbs. to 2 HP/4000 lbs.)	$1,000	$3,000
Drum Dollies (30 to 55 Gallon)	$45	$60
Drum Dumper (750 to 1500 lbs. cap./36" to 60" dump ht.)	$2,500	$3,500
Drum Hand Truck (Steel–55 Gallon)	$180	$250
Drum Hand Truck (Aluminum–55 Gallon)	$350	$600
Gantry Cranes (12' to 15' ht./7' to 10' I-beam) (above price includes I-beam trolley, chain hoist not included)	$1,200	$1,800
Hand-Trucks (Steel 48"–52" H x 16"–18" W)	$100	$160
Hand-Trucks (Aluminum 48"–52" H x 16"–18" W)	$120	$225
Jib Crane—Floor Mounted (500 to 2000 lbs.) (chain hoist and concrete footings not included)	$1,600	$2,200
Jib Crane—Floor Mounted (2000 to 6000 lbs.) (chain hoist and concrete footings not included)	$2,600	$6,500
Platform Trucks (24" W x 36" L to 36" W x 72" L)	$250	$500
Picking Carts—Two Shelf (24" W x 36" L to 36" W x 48" L)	$150	$350
Rolling Safety Ladders w/Handrails (2–4 step)	$150	$350
Rolling Safety Ladders w/Handrails (5–10 step)	$400	$700
Rolling Safety Ladders w/Handrails (11–16 step)	$900	$1,200
Scissor Lifts/Pallet Positioners	$1,200	$3,600
Stock Picking Cart w/Spring-Loaded Stepladder	$500	$800
Self Dumping Hoppers (1 to 5 cu. yds.)	$600	$1,400
Tilt Trucks (0.5 to 2.5 cu. yds.)	$1,000	$2,000

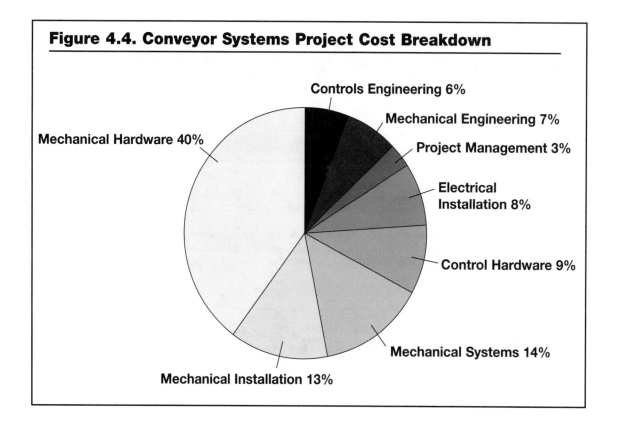

Figure 4.4. Conveyor Systems Project Cost Breakdown

Controls Engineering 6%

Mechanical Engineering 7%

Project Management 3%

Electrical Installation 8%

Control Hardware 9%

Mechanical Systems 14%

Mechanical Installation 13%

Mechanical Hardware 40%

Step 3. Identify Storage Equipment Costs. Costs of storage equipment can be obtained from manufacturers and industrial equipment suppliers. Quantity discounts are usually available on large installations. Used storage equipment in good condition can be considered in the bidding process, but only if it meets specifications. Getting seismic code approval for used rack can be difficult. **Figure 4.5** shows some typical cost estimates of new storage modules.

For pallet rack systems, the cost of materials differs between structural steel and roll-formed beams and uprights. In the past, roll-formed steel rack systems were less expensive than structural steel rack systems. The difference in prices has narrowed to as little as 10%. Structural steel racks are more likely to withstand impact and damage compared to roll-formed racks. When a roll-formed upright is struck, its load-carrying capacity is reduced. The load should be removed immediately and the damaged upright replaced. Additional pallet rack options will increase costs. Some of these options include safety bars, upright protectors, and decking.

Costs increase when shelving and flow racks are used to support mezzanines or used as part of a specialized system as in pick-to-light applications.

Step 4. Determine and Identify Other Special Costs. These are miscellaneous costs incurred in the start-up of a new or improved warehouse. They include the following:

Planning and Design Costs. These are estimated expenses incurred by the study and implementation team to assess, design, justify, and implement the new design. These include

Figure 4.5. Storage Equipment Costs

Pallet Rack:	Lower Range	Upper Range
Rack priced per pallet position including floor positions/assumption of 4–5 pallet levels high/standard 48"x 40" pallets with maximum load of 2500# per pallet/structural or roll-formed steel		
Standard Selective Pallet Rack	$35	$50
Double Deep Pallet Rack	$40	$55
Drive-In Pallet Rack (2 Deep)	$65	$80
Drive-In Pallet Rack (3 Deep)	$55	$75
Drive-In Pallet Rack (4+ Deep)	$45	$60
Drive-Through Pallet Rack (2 Deep)	$70	$90
Drive-Through Pallet Rack (3 Deep)	$60	$80
Drive-Through Pallet Rack (4+ Deep)	$50	$70
Push-Back Pallet Rack (2 Deep)	$90	$110
Push-Back Pallet Rack (3 Deep)	$125	$135
Push-Back Pallet Rack (4 Deep)	$145	$155
Push-Back Pallet Rack (5 Deep)	$165	$175
Gravity Flow Pallet Rack (2 Deep)	$100	$150
Gravity Flow Pallet Rack (3+ Deep)	$250	$350
Stacking Frames (2,000# Per Frame, to Stack 5 High):		
Frames for Wood Pallets	$60	$100
With Steel "Pallet" Bases	$90	$160
Pallet Rack Options:		
Wire Deck Sections (Each Pallet)	$14	$36
Pallet Supports (Per Pair)	$12	$25
Upright Post Guard (Each)	$9	$18
End-of-Aisle Rack Protectors (One at the End of Each Row of Back-to-Back Rack)	$150	$300
Cantilever Rack (Pipe/Tube/Bar Lumber):		
Heavy-duty cantilever rack priced per 8'0" wide bay x the heights listed below		
8'-0" Height		
Single-Sided Cantilever (Four Sets Of Arms)	$400	$600
Double-Sided Cantilever (Eight Sets Of Arms)	$600	$800
12'-0" Height:		
Single-Sided Cantilever (Six Sets Of Arms)	$550	$750
Double-Sided Cantilever (Twelve Sets Of Arms)	$950	$1,150
16'-0" Height:		
Single-Sided Cantilever (Eight Sets Of Arms)	$1,050	$1,250
Double-Sided Cantilever (Sixteen Sets Of Arms)	$1,550	$1,750
Drum Stacking Racks:		
Stacking frames for horizontal floor storage		
2-Drum Stacking Rack Unit (55 Gallon)	$45	$75
3-Drum Stacking Rack Unit (55 Gallon) (13" H x 48" W x 30" D)	$65	$95

Figure 4.5. Storage Equipment Costs (continued)

Open Type Shelving:	Lower Range	Upper Range
Steel-clip type or nut and bolt shelving units 36"–48" W x 12"–24" D x 72"–96" H with six shelves per unit		
Light to Medium Duty (20–22 gauge)	$75	$150
Heavy Duty (18 gauge)	$175	$350

Closed Type Shelving:	Lower Range	Upper Range
Steel-clip type or nut and bolt shelving units 36"–48" W x 12"–24" D x 72"–96" H with six shelves per unit		
Light to Medium Duty (20–22 gauge)	$110	$220
Heavy Duty (18 gauge)	$240	$480

Open Welded Wire Shelving:	Lower Range	Upper Range
Chrome-Plated or Epoxy-Coated Welded Steel Wire 60"–84" H x 14"–24" D x 36"–48" W w/4–5 Shelves Each Unit	$275	$400
Stainless Steel Welded Wire 60"–84" H x 14"–24" D x 36"–48" W w/4–5 Shelves Each Unit	$850	$1,250

Storage Cabinets:	Lower Range	Upper Range
36"–48" W x 18"–24" D x 72"–84" H with 4–6 adjustable steel shelves		
Light to Medium Duty	$280	$460
Heavy Duty	$650	$950

Steel Lockers:	Lower Range	Upper Range
Single-Tier Lockers (One Opening Per Unit) (60"–72" H x 12"–15" W x 12"–18" D)	$100	$140
Double-Tier Lockers Per Opening (Two Openings Per Unit) (60"–72" H x 12"–15" W x 12"–18" D)	$60	$80
Six-Tier Lockers Per Opening (Six Openings Per Unit) (High-Density Polyethylene 9"–15" H x 15"–20" W x 20"–28" L)	$25	$35

Tote Boxes:	Lower Range	Upper Range
Nesting Totes (Suitable for Picking) (High-Density Polyethylene 9"–15" H x 15"–20" W x 20"–28" L)	$7	$18
Nesting Totes (Suitable for Picking) (Corrugated Plastic 9"–15" H x 15"–20" W x 20"–28" L)	$7	$14
Optional Cover (Removable Lid) for Above Tote	$2	$4
Nest/Reverse Orientation Stack Totes w/o Cover (Suitable for Picking and/or Shipping with Optional Lid) (High-Density Polyethylene 9"–15" H x 15"–20" W x 20"–28" L)	$8	$22
Optional Cover (removable lid) for Above Tote	$4	$6
Stack and Nest with Integral Hinged Cover (Suitable for Picking and Shipping) (High-Density Polyethylene 9"–15" H x 15"–20" W x 20"–28" L)	$12	$28

Plastic Pallets:	Lower Range	Upper Range
48" x 40" Thermoformed, Rotationally Molded, or Injection Molded, Each (For USDA or FDA Approved Pallets, Use the Higher End of the Price Spectrum)	$45	$90

Figure 4.5. Storage Equipment Costs (continued)

Shelf Bins (Heavy-Duty Plastic):	Lower Range	Upper Range
Nestable one-piece shelf bins, typically polypropylene		
12" Deep:		
Small (3"–4" W x 4"–5" H) Each	$1.50	$2.00
Large (6"–8" W x 4"–5" H) Each	$2.50	$3.75
18" Deep:		
Small (4"–6" W x 4"–5" H) Each	$2.00	$3.00
Large (6"–12" W x 4"–5" H) Each	$4.50	$6.00
24" Deep:		
Small (3"–4" W x 4"–5" H) Each	$3.50	$5.50
Large (6"–12" W x 4"–5" H) Each	$5.50	$7.75
Shelf Bins (Light-Duty Plastic):		
Nestable one-piece shelf bins, typically polyethylene		
12" Deep:		
Small (3"–4" W x 4"–5" H) Each	$1.00	$1.50
Large (6"–8" W x 4"–5" H) Each	$1.25	$1.75
18" Deep:		
Small (4"–6" W x 4"–5" H) Each	$1.50	$2.00
Large (6"–12" W x 4"–5" H) Each	$2.50	$3.75
24" Deep:		
Small (4"–6" W x 4"–5" H) Each	$3.00	$4.50
Large (6"–12" W x 4"–5" H) Each	$3.75	$5.75
Shelf Bins (Light-Duty Corrugated Paper):		
Knocked-down one-piece shelf bins, corrugated paper die-cut construction		
12" Deep:		
Small (3"–4" W x 4"–5" H) Each	$0.40	$0.60
Large (6"–8" W x 4"–5" H) Each	$0.60	$0.90
18" Deep:		
Small (4"–6" W x 4"–5" H) Each	$0.80	$1.20
Large (6"–12" W x 4"–5" H) Each	$1.20	$1.70
24" Deep:		
Small (4"–6" W x 4"–5" H) Each	$1.20	$1.90
Large (6"–12" W x 4"–5" H) Each	$1.90	$2.50
Louvered-Panel Compatible Bins:		
One-piece stackable bins, typically polypropylene		
3" H x 4" W x 5" L Each	$0.70	$0.90
3" H x 4" W x 7" L Each	$1.20	$1.50
4" H x 4" W x 11" L Each	$1.75	$2.20
5" H x 5" W x 11" L Each	$2.90	$3.75

Figure 4.5. Storage Equipment Costs (continued)

Louvered-Panel Compatible Bins (continued):	Lower Range	Upper Range
One-piece stackable bins, typically polypropylene		
5" H x 11" W x 11" L Each	$4.25	$5.35
5" H x 16" W x 11" L Each	$6.25	$7.80
7" H x 8" W x 11" L Each	$4.75	$6.00
7" H x 8" W x 15" L Each	$5.50	$6.90
7" H x 16" W x 15" L Each	$7.70	$9.60
9" H x 8" W x 18" L Each	$8.50	$10.60
11" H x 16" W x 18" L Each	$12.75	$16.00

Perforated Louvered Panels for Plastic Bins:	Lower Range	Upper Range
(Painted Steel) Available in a variety of sizes per square foot	$10	$25

Wide-Span Storage Rack:	Lower Range	Upper Range
Typically used for hand-loaded static carton storage; i.e., pick-pack or archives — Priced per bay 96" W x 96" H x 24"–36" D w/4 shelves		
Wide-Span Unit (Particle Board Deck)	$350	$450
Wide-Span Unit (Corrugated Steel Deck)	$450	$550
Wide-Span Unit (Wire Deck)	$550	$650

Carton Flow Rack:	Lower Range	Upper Range
10' D x 5' W x 8' H — 5 Shelves w/4 Lanes Each, Priced Per Bay Carton Flow Unit	$1,000	$1,500
10' D x 8' W x 8' H — 5 Shelves w/4 Lanes Each, Priced Per Bay Carton Flow Unit	$1,600	$2,000

Flammable Liquid Storage Cabinets:	Lower Range	Upper Range
Full-Size w/Standard Doors (60"–72" H x 36"–48" W x 18"–36" D)	$1,200	$1,500
Full-Size w/Self-Closing Doors (60"–72" H x 36"–48" W x 18"–36" D)	$1,600	$1,900
Standard-Size w/Standard Doors (36"–48" H x 36"–48" W x 18"–24" D)	$600	$800
Standard-Size w/Self-Closing Doors (36"–48" H x 36"–48" W x 18"–24" D)	$700	$900

High-Density Storage Drawer Modules:	Lower Range	Upper Range
Bench Height (33" H x 30" W x 28" D w/4–8 Drawers)	$600	$1,000
Counter Height (45" H x 30" W x 28" D w/6–12 Drawers)	$900	$1,400
Full Height (60" H x 30" W x 28" D)	$1,200	$1,800
Drawer Divider Kits (Priced Per Drawer)		
4–9 Compartments	$12	$25
12–48 Compartments	$30	$65

Carousels:	Lower Range	Upper Range
Horizontal Carousels Per Carrier (Common Horizontal Carousel Configurations Consist of 30–60 Carriers Per Carousel, With 2–4 Carousels Per Pod)	$750	$1,000
Vertical Carousels Per Vertical Foot (Common Vertical Carousels Range From 15'–30' in Height)	$1,500	$3,000

costs for the in-house study team and any external consultants that were hired specifically for the redesign initiative. **Figure 4.6** is an example of planning and design costs incurred by a retail chain redesigning the docks and order processing area to start new cross docking practices. Logistics consultants were used to develop the cross dock operation and procedures, to act as liaisons between the chain's suppliers and management, to evaluate information systems equipment bids, and to help justify the entire project. An independent consultant infuses objec-

Figure 4.6. Sample Planning and Design Costs

Cost Elements	Labor Hours	Cost Per Hour	Total Costs
Planning and Design Cost			
In-House Study & Implementation Team			
Logistics Manager	240	$50	$12,000
Operations Manager	230	$40	$9,200
Procurement Manager	250	$40	$10,000
Merchandising Manager	150	$40	$6,000
Accounting Manager	50	$35	$1,750
Information Systems Manager	150	$35	$5,250
Engineers	300	$25	$7,500
Others	80	$25	$2,000
External Consultants			
Logistics Consultant	flat rate	N/A	$60,000
Information Systems Consultant	300	$200	$60,000
Training Costs			$30,000
Total Planning and Design Costs			**$203,700**

Source: *Making the Move to Cross Docking* (2000, p.115). Copyright Warehousing Education and Research Council, Oak Brooke, IL. All rights reserved.

tivity, knowledge, and experience into the design project. They also have design tools, such as CAD and simulation, which may not be available in-house.

Training Costs. These are costs incurred in developing training materials and the actual training of personnel on the new concepts and procedures.

Information Systems. Capital costs for information systems may or may not be a significant factor of overall costs. Some designs may require complex warehouse management systems to run their operations. These management systems include the software and hardware that keep track of daily operations. Different software programs provide many warehouse applications, such as:

- Inventory management

- Inventory planning and forecasting

- Customer services/order processing

- Electronic data interchange

- Purchasing

- Transportation rate calculation and analyses

- Warehouse operations analyses

- Productivity analyses and reporting

- Facility location modeling.

Logistics software is available for mainframe, minicomputer, and microcomputer systems. Mainframe-based software ranges from a minimum of $2,000 for a basic application up to millions of dollars for an entire warehouse system. Minicomputer system software ranges from $700 per application to over a million dollars for an entire system. Software for microcomputer or PC (personal computer) systems may start at under $100 without any hardware. Prices vary significantly depending on the number of warehouse applications, the complexity of the application, the type and quantity of hardware, the training, the frequency of updates, and the technical support.

Miscellaneous Costs. These costs include dock equipment, fire protection systems, security systems, painting and sealing, mezzanines, and office equipment that may be a part of the new design. Typically, warehouses are considered as an ordinary hazard among commercial installations. The appropriate hazard rating will depend on what is being stored. Ceiling and in-rack sprinklers, if required, should be designed to a density (gallons per minute per square foot) according to National Fire Protection Association (NFPA) standards. ESFR (early suppression/fast response) is a fire protection system that eliminates in-rack sprinklers. Essentially, this uses a sprinkler head in the ceiling, which releases tremendous quantities of water. The sprinkler heads cannot be over 40 feet and stacking cannot be over 35 feet. In a new warehouse, ESFR may provide cost savings because in-rack sprinklers are not required. However, the base system can get more expensive if booster pumps or fire pumps are required to deliver the volume of water that ESFR requires. Nevertheless, ESFR systems offer reduced maintenance and more flexibility in the layout as opposed to in-rack sprinkler systems.

Figures 4.7 and **4.8** list various miscellaneous costs involved in warehouse design. **Figure 4.7** shows dock equipment costs, while **Figure 4.8** shows other special costs.

Operating Costs

The daily operation of a warehouse has many costs. They should not be neglected in analyzing alternatives. A storage system may have the lowest capital costs but have the highest operating costs. Operating costs vary from warehouse to warehouse. To facilitate the process, examples are provided as a guide in calculating costs that are specific to a warehouse. These examples have been provided for illustrative purposes only.[1]

Cost models to facilitate this process have already been designed. The user essentially "fills in the blanks" where appropriate. Their configurations may differ slightly, but the basic cost elements remain the same. A partial list is provided at the end of this section. The follow-

Figure 4.7. Dock Equipment Costs

Dock Levelers:	Lower Range	Upper Range
Mechanical Pit Leveler	$2,250	$6,500
Pneumatic Pit Leveler	$2,500	$5,500
Hydraulic Pit Leveler	$3,500	$8,000
Edge of Dock Leveler	$750	$2,250

Vehicle Restraint Systems:	Lower Range	Upper Range
May vary widely due to potential for complex wiring, interlocks to the dock levelers, door openers, etc.		
Manual Restraints	$1,500	$2,500
Automatic Restraints	$3,000	$6,000
Wheel Restraints	$8,000	$12,000

Dock Boards/Plates:	Lower Range	Upper Range
Aluminum Board (to 5000 lbs. cap. with Welded Curbs)	$500	$1,200
Aluminum Board (to 10,000 lbs. cap. with Welded Curbs)	$750	$1,750
Aluminum Plate (to 5,000 lbs. cap., No Curbs)	$350	$750
Steel Board (to 10,000 lbs. cap. with Welded Curbs)	$500	$1,200

Impactable Dock Door:	Lower Range	Upper Range
Manual Operation	$2,000	$3,500
Automatic Operation	$3,000	$4,500

Seals, Shelters, and Restraints:	Lower Range	Upper Range
Standard Door Seal	$750	$1,500
Standard Door Shelter	$1,200	$4,800
Semi-Automatic Truck Restraint	$3,400	$4,700

Barrier Rail Systems:	Lower Range	Upper Range
Typically used to protect pedestrian paths and equipment from lift-truck impact (Priced per linear foot)		
48" High Protective "Highway Type" Barrier Rail System w/3 Rails	$50	$65
48" High Protective "Highway Type" Barrier Rail System w/2 Rails	$40	$50
18" High Protective "Highway Type" Barrier Rail System w/1 Rail	$30	$40

Dock Lights and Fans:	Lower Range	Upper Range
Adjustable Arm-Mounted Dock Lights (Low End of Price Scale for Incandescent/High End for Halogen)	$120	$180
Adjustable Arm-Mounted Dock Fan (18" 3 Speed/10,000 Cubic Feet Per Minute)	$275	$325

Dock Scales:	Lower Range	Upper Range
5,000 lbs. Capacity Floor Scale (Mild Steel) (48" x 48" to 60" x 60" w/3" Profile)	$2,500	$3,000
5,000 lbs. Capacity Floor Scale (Stainless Steel) (48" x 48" to 60" x 60" w/3" Profile)	$4,500	$5,500

Figure 4.8. Other Special Costs

Mezzanines, Catwalks, and Storage Platforms Pre-Engineered Structural Steel Systems:	Lower Range	Upper Range
8' Underclearance, 9' Deck Height, 150–200 PSF Capacity, Priced Per Square Foot. Price includes Handrail, Toeguard, and One Stairway. (Lower Range for Standard Spans, Upper Range for Wide Spans Between Columns)		
Mezzanine (Per Sq. Ft.) (3/4" Tongue and Groove Plywood Over Corrugated Steel Roof Deck)	$16	$20
Resin Impregnated Wood Deck — Add to Prices Above	$2	$3
Mezzanine (Per Sq. Ft.) (Perforated Steel Plank Deck)	$13	$17
Mezzanine (Per Sq. Ft.) (Solid Steel Plank Deck)	$14	$18
Additional Stair and Landing (Each)	$2,500	$3,500
Mezzanine-Edge Safety Gates:	**Lower Range**	**Upper Range**
Single Pallet Width	$4,000	$5,000
Dual Pallet Width	$5,200	$6,000
Side Access	$6,000	$7,500
Security Enclosures & In-Plant Buildings Wire Security Partitions:	**Lower Range**	**Upper Range**
Priced per linear foot — without doors or roof		
8'-High Wire Partition	$13	$17
10'-High Wire Partition	$16	$20
12'-High Wire Partition	$18	$22
Wire Partition Options:	**Lower Range**	**Upper Range**
Wire Roof (Per Sq. Ft.)	$3	$5
Single Swing Doors (Each)	$400	$600
Double Swing Doors (Each Set)	$800	$1,000
Slide Door (Each)	$500	$750
3" Thick 4' x 8' Wall Panel Systems	$55	$80
Corrugated Steel Roof Deck and Acoustical Tile Ceiling/Grid (Sq. Ft.)	$6	$8
Doors (Steel or Solid Core Wood)	$300	$400
Windows (Factory Glazed)	$100	$150

Above pricing for class "A" fire rated gypsum-based wall systems with an STC rating of 30 to 35. For panel STC ratings of 50 to 60, multiply total structure cost as calculated above by a factor of 3.5.

Prices do not include electrical wiring or H.V.A.C. systems. Add 25% of building value for factory-wired electrical package including lights, receptacles, and switches.

Please note: Pre-arranged modular construction may allow accelerated depreciation schedules to be applied. Check with your accounting department.

Workstations — Benches and Tables:	**Lower Range**	**Upper Range**
Work Benches (30" to 36" D x 48" to 72" W)	$300	$600
Electronic or Assembly Work Benches (30" to 36" D x 48" to 72" W)	$800	$1,600
Packing Tables (30" to 36" D x 48" to 72" W)	$700	$1,400
Production Tables (30" to 48" D x 72" to 120" W)	$400	$800

Figure 4.8. Other Special Costs (continued)

Industrial Seating:	Lower Range	Upper Range
Bench Chairs (Seat Ht. 19" to 37")	$250	$375
Bench Stools (Seat Ht. 19" to 37")	$125	$175

Painting and Sealing:	Lower Range	Upper Range
Costs can be affected by many factors, including age and condition of the surfaces, equipment to be moved, and off-hours work		

Walls (Per Square Foot):		Lower Range	Upper Range
Masonry Block			
Filler		$0.24	$0.38
Finish (2 coats)	Latex	$0.18	$0.32
	Oil	$0.18	$0.50
	Epoxy	$0.30	$0.60
Sheet Rock			
Prime (2 coats)	Latex	$0.55	$0.75
	Oil	$0.60	$0.80
	Epoxy	$0.65	$0.85

Ceilings (Per Square Foot):	Lower Range	Upper Range
Open Joists Sprayed — 1 coat	$0.55	$0.75

Floors (Per Square Foot)		Lower Range	Upper Range
Preparation — Shot Blasting		$0.50	$0.75
Paint	Enamel — 1 coat	$0.35	
	Epoxy	$0.50	
	Non-Skid Epoxy	$2.50	$4.50
	Sealer — Dust control	$0.35	
Lines — per linear foot 4" wide		$1.25	

ing cost components are part of a model developed by Thomas Speh for calculating warehousing costs.[2] The steps for developing operating costs are to:

1. Determine annual costs for direct storage

2. Determine annual costs for direct handling

3. Determine annual costs for operating administration

4. Determine annual costs for general administration

5. Validate the data

6. Allocate costs for analysis.

Step 1. Determine Annual Costs for Direct Storage. Storage expenses are incurred with the ownership (or rental), operation, and maintenance of the facility regardless of whether or not any product in the warehouse ever moves. After determining the amount of space, the next step is to allocate these annual costs and expenses. For an existing facility, these expenses can be identified from a company's general ledger or from financial statements of operations. For a new facility, research may be required to acquire accurate costs for utilities and other storage related services. Some third-party providers use costs from existing facilities that they operate in the same area. These specific storage-related categories include:

• Rent or depreciation and interest. If the building is rented, the cost would be the total rental fee for the year. If the building is owned, there are several approaches available. Consider the replacement costs of facilities where appropriate. The International Warehouse Logistics Association suggests the approach shown in **Figure 4.9**.

• Real estate taxes. If rented, the expenses would be the proportion of the real estate taxes that the lessee is responsible for according to the terms of the contract.

• Insurance related to the physical facility.

• Exterior and interior maintenance of the physical facility. This includes facility modification expenses that are related to the maintenance of the building.

Figure 4.9. A Worksheet for Calculating Costs of Ownership

Owned Building

_____B1. Current Market Value (of distribution facility) including net selling price, owned racking equipment, and other installed equipment

_____B2. Book Value (from financial statements)

_____B3. Realizable Gain (line B1 minus line B2)

Annual Market Rent Achievable

_____B4. Funds that would be received each month by renting out total distribution space (estimate should be based on current local market rates)

_____B5. Annual Rent (line B4 times 12)

Opportunity Cost

_____B6. Realizable Gain (from line B3)

X_____B7. Corporate Cost of Capital or Current Interest Rates

=_____B8. Yearly Revenue (line B6 times line B7)

_____B9. Greater of Line B8 or Line B5.

This figure represents the annual revenue foregone by ownership.

- Grounds maintenance, including landscaping and snow removal.

- Storage equipment depreciation, interest, and maintenance. This calculation involves installed equipment related to storage, such as pallet racks, shelving, case flow racks, carousels, etc.

- Utilities. This includes heat, electricity, water, and sewage charges.

- Security. This includes charges relating to the protection of the facility and its contents.

- Pest control.

- Other facility expenses not captured in the above categories. In some partially empty facilities, there may be specific costs for carrying additional square footage to allow for expansion.

- The sum of all of these expenses determines the total annual cost of direct storage expenses for a facility.

Step 2. Determine Annual Costs for Direct Handling. Handling expenses are derived from the activities that are directly associated with the movement of products into and out of the warehouse. For an existing facility, these expenses can be identified from a company's general ledger or from financial statements of operations. For a new facility, some research may be necessary to acquire accurate costs for labor expenses and other handling-related services. Some third-party providers use costs from existing facilities operating in the same area. Handling expenses are listed under three main categories:

Figure 4.10. Average Hourly Wages of Warehousing Jobs By Geographic Region and by Business

2002 Average Hourly Wages by Geographic Region

Warehouse Title	Overall	Northeast	Midwest	South	West
Forklift Operator	$12.19	$12.49	$12.65	$11.59	$12.14
Order Filler	11.38	11.16	11.66	11.22	11.27
Shipping/Receiving Clerk	12.02	12.57	12.20	11.39	12.09
Customer Service Representative	12.50	12.40	12.72	11.95	13.08

2002 Average Hourly Wages by Business

Warehouse Title	Manufacturer	Retailer	Wholesaler/ Distributor	3rd-Party Public	3rd-Party Contract	3rd-Party Mix	Other
Forklift Operator	$13.77	$12.17	$12.24	$11.65	$10.82	$11.31	$12.31
Order Filler	12.93	10.95	11.56	11.34	10.20	9.33	10.36
Shipping/Receiving Clerk	13.80	10.54	12.26	11.70	11.17	11.98	10.88
Customer Service Representative	14.98	10.48	12.81	11.37	12.19	12.16	12.04

Source: *Warehousing Salaries and Wages* (2002 Data). Copyright Warehousing Education and Research Council, Oak Brook, IL. All rights reserved.

Warehouse labor. This includes:

- Direct payment made to warehouse employees and part-time labor. This includes wages, bonuses, and overtime. **Figure 4.10** lists hourly wages of different warehousing jobs based on a 2002 survey of 382 warehouses sponsored by the Warehousing Education and Research Council. These wages are actual straight pay and do not include overtime premiums, shift differentials, bonuses, or any other incentives or variable pay components.[3]

- Company-paid benefits. This includes insurance, pensions, uniforms, and other fringes provided by the company.

- Compensated time off, such as vacations, sick days, holidays, or jury duty.

- Statutory local, state, and federal payroll taxes.

- Purchased (temporary) labor.

- Fees and compensated time. This includes company-paid expenses for in-house training programs, fees to attend seminars, etc.

Handling equipment. These expenses include the rental or depreciation and interest, fuel, maintenance, and other expenses associated with lift trucks, attachments, and other special purpose handling equipment, such as conveyors, stretch wrap machines, palletizers, automated guided vehicles (AGVs), air compressors, etc. At an SKU level of analysis, unique handling characteristics of an item may increase this expense category. For example, if a product is received and shipped in drums, then a special lift truck attachment may be required, thus increasing equipment costs.

Other handling expenses. These can include:

- Pallet purchase and repair.

- Supplies. This includes items used in the handling process, such as stretch wrap, tape, labels, staples, dunnage, cartons, and packing supplies.

- Detention/demurrage. These expenses are charged by both railroad and motor carriers for delays.

- Recouping warehouse damage. These are the expenses involved in refurbishing damaged merchandise to its original condition.

- Trash hauling. This includes the commercial or municipal charges for trash removal.

- Other costs that are not reflected in the above categories.

The sum of all of these expenses determines the annual costs of direct handling expenses for a facility.

Step 3. Determine Annual Costs for Operating Administration. These are costs incurred in supporting a warehouse operation, and are generally tied to a specific warehouse. If the warehouse were to be closed, these expenses would disappear. For an existing facility, these expenses can be identified from the general ledger or from financial statements of operations. For a new facility, research may be necessary to acquire accurate costs for operating administrative expenses. The following categories are included in this cost module:

- Supervisory salaries. Personnel in this group include the general manager, warehouse supervisors, office managers, traffic managers, and clerical managers.

- Clerical salaries. Note that some companies may assign these to specific warehouse activities.

- Purchased (temporary) labor relating to operating administration.

- Office equipment rental or depreciation and interest, and maintenance for computers, copiers, etc.

- Office maintenance such as janitorial service.

- Communication expenses, including telephone, facsimile, supplies, and other communications-related expenses of a specific warehouse.

- Postage, including fees and other delivery charges.

- Printing costs.

- Office supplies.

- Data processing involving computer hardware, software, programming, supplies, and computer services developed and used in a specific warehouse. Expenses including rent, depreciation and interest on the equipment, the costs of dedicated phone lines, computer forms, labor to maintain the equipment, and other costs contracted for data processing.

- Legal and professional costs incurred for work by outside professionals whose scope and cost of work can be allocated to a facility.

- Taxes and licenses, including occupational licenses and franchise taxes.

- Travel expenses by facility operating personnel.

- Personal property taxes assessed on office furniture and equipment.

- Insurance and claims, including premiums for liability, personal property, legal liability, property damage, etc.

- Losses due to damages, shortages, and payment from mistakes made in the warehouse.

- Other expenses not included in the above categories.

The total of all of these expenses is the annual operating administrative expenses for a facility.

Step 4. Determine Annual Costs for General Administration. In contrast to operating administrative expenses, general administrative expenses are not directly related to the operation of a specific warehouse. Instead, they support the overall mission of the company. If one of the warehouses owned by the company is closed, then most of these expenses would still be incurred. Exceptions do occur where a portion of the general administrative expenses may be specific to a given facility. Management decides the proper allocation of general administration costs to warehousing operations.

Some of these cost elements may be unique to third-party providers and are not experienced by private warehouses. For example, third-party contractors have marketing, sales, and advertising expenses, which are not required for private warehouses.

For an existing facility, these expenses may be identified from the company's general ledger or from financial statements of operations. For a new facility, research may be necessary to acquire accurate costs for general administrative expenses. The categories for general administration include:

- Executive salaries, bonuses, fringe benefits, compensated time off, and payroll taxes paid to company executives (director of logistics, vice president of logistics) and corporate managers who devote some or all of their time to warehousing.

- Marketing salaries (applied to third-party providers, unless private warehouses have marketing personnel involved in warehousing).

- Support salaries representing an allocation of clerical, accounting, legal, real estate, human resources, and other services that support the mission of the warehouse in some capacity.

- Office space and equipment expenses.

- General office operations, including costs for operating the corporate office — such as telephone, postage, printing, utilities, and courier services — that may be eliminated if a specific warehouse is closed.

- Data processing, including appropriate portions of equipment rental or depreciation and interest, maintenance, and software expense in operating a specific facility.

- Taxes, including appropriate portions of general property taxes, real estate taxes for office space, and licenses.

- Legal and professional fees, including fees for lawyers, consultants, and other professionals paid by the corporate logistics office for a specific warehouse.

- Selling and advertising expenses, including advertising space costs, sales promotion expense, sales commissions, and other related expenses. This category is most relevant to third-party providers.

- Travel expenses, including travel by corporate logistics management related to a specific warehouse.

- Dues, subscriptions, and educational expenses.

Figure 4.11. Example of Annual Operating Expenses by Category For a Sample Warehouse (For use with calculations on pages 112–114)

Direct Handling Expenses	
Equipment:	
Equipment depreciation and interest	$355,400
Batteries/chargers/fuel	13,000
Forklift maintenance	70,100
Supplies and parts: handling equipment	45,400
Labor:	
Hourly wages	1,301,000
Hourly benefits	180,500
Purchased labor	52,000
Hourly payroll taxes	289,500
Paid vacations/holidays: hourly	24,000
Other handling expenses	41,600
Total Direct Handling Expenses	**$2,372,500**
Direct Storage Expenses	
Facility depreciation and interest	665,100
Real estate taxes	27,000
Utilities, including freezer and coolers	186,200
Insurance: facility	34,400
Exterior maintenance/grounds	28,600
Total Direct Storage Expenses	**$941,300**
Operating and General Administrative Expenses	
Operating:	
Supervisory salaries and fringes	210,000
Clerical supervision: salaries and fringes	80,000
Off-site travel: warehouse/support management	30,000
Training: management and supervisory	45,000
Information processing/computer	60,000
General:	
Executive/officer salaries and fringes	130,000
Executive/officer travel	40,000
Selling expense	65,000
Total Operating and General	**$660,000**

Source: *Using Modeling to Solve Warehousing Problems* (1998, p.36). Copyright Warehousing Education and Research Council, Oak Brook, IL. All rights reserved.

• Donations.

• Personnel expenses involved in recruiting, hiring, and testing new warehouse employees by corporate personnel.

• Bad debt expenses for third-party providers for uncollectible accounts.

• Any other non-operating expenses not described in the above categories.

The sum of all of these expenses determines the annual general administration expenses.

Step 5. Validate the Data. Whenever possible, reconfigured expenses should be validated and verified against historical costs. The total numbers calculated above should be checked against financial statements, profit and loss statements, or other documents to substantiate the model's validity. This is a key step when developing new-facility costs. Third-party contractors validate their cost models against warehouses or customers for whom they operate in a similar area.

Figure 4.11 shows a sample configuration of warehouse-related expenses according to the four main categories previously described. This cost configuration will be used as a working example in developing unit costs. The unit cost calculations in Step 6 assume a collection of SKUs that are similar in storage and handling requirements. If products vary in size and storage configuration, a more detailed breakdown of costs will be required.

Step 6. Allocate Costs for Analysis. In comparing alternative investments, it is often necessary to allocate costs to specific units to use in the analysis. In this step, we show how to determine:

a. Storage costs per square foot

b. Storage rate per unit

c. Handling costs per hour

d. Handling rate per unit.

a. Storage Costs Per Square Foot. Total storage expenses are calculated by adding the direct storage expenses plus an allocation of operating administrative (OA) and general administrative (GA) expenses. Using **Figure 4.11** as an example, if a 50-50 allocation is used for storage and handling, then total storage expenses for the entire facility based on a storage space of 120,000 square feet would be:

Direct Storage Expenses (From Step 1)		$941,300
50% of OA and GA total (From Step 3 & 4)	+	$330,000
Total Storage Expenses		$1,271,300
Total Gross Square Feet	÷	120,000
Storage Costs Per Gross Square Foot		$10.59

For third-party providers, the Total Storage Expenses will also include a percentage for profit. If analysis is required at the SKU level, each SKU will require different types of storage modules depending on stackability, size, shape, and inventory characteristics. The storage expenses per square foot will depend on the space occupied by storage modules and the number of modules storing a specific SKU. See the warehouse space calculations in the previous chapter.

b. Storage Rate Per Unit. There are several methods for calculating monthly storage rates or storage costs per square foot per unit. Third-party providers use different formulas depending on billing options. For this discussion, monthly storage rates per unit can be calculated by using the following (based on a peak inventory of 1,340,000 units):

Storage Cost Per Gross Square Foot (From Step 6-a)	$10.59
Divide by Months in Year	÷ 12
Monthly Storage Costs Per Square Foot	$0.882
Estimated Peak Inventory During Month	1,340,000
Total Gross Square Feet (From Step 6-a)	÷ 120,000
Units Stored Per Gross Square Foot	11.17
Monthly Storage Rate Per Unit	$0.079

(Monthly Storage Costs ÷ Units Stored Per Gross Square Foot)

A more detailed analysis of rates at the SKU level should include the impact of inventory turns. Annual storage expenses are usually based on the annual turns or average inventory for an SKU. If a third-party operator has an SKU with low turnover, the storage charges may be higher than for a fast-moving SKU. In some cases, if access to a product is seldom required, the third-party operator may decide to bulk stack these SKUs to reduce the square footage required.

c. Handling Costs Per Hour. Using **Figure 4.11** as an example, if a 50-50 allocation is used for storage and handling and based on 110,000 direct labor hours, then the total handling expenses for the entire facility would be:

Direct Handling Costs (From Step 2)	$2,372,500
50% of OA and GA total (From Step 3 & 4)	+ $330,000
Total Handling Costs	$2,702,500
Total Warehouse Labor Hours	÷ 110,000
Handling Costs Per Hour	$24.57

For third-party providers, the Total Handling Costs will also include a percentage for profit.

d. Handling Rate Per Unit. The handling rate or handling costs per hour per unit depends on the annual throughput of the warehouse. This can be calculated as total receipts plus total shipments for the year, divided by two. For a third-party contractor, this is critical information that dictates the cost for services. A high throughput volume means costs are allocated over more SKUs and will consequently lower the cost per SKU. Conversely, a low throughput increases cost per SKU and may even negate the need for a third-party provider. Some contracts specify a rate based on a minimum volume that will move through the facility, and the customer pays a penalty when throughput falls below that minimum. For this discussion, handling rates per SKU can be calculated by using the following (based on an annual throughput of 1,200,000 units):

Handling Costs Per Hour (From Step 6-c)	$24.57
Annual Throughput in Units	1,200,000
Annual Warehouse Labor Hours (From Step 6-c) ÷	110,000
Throughput Units Per Labor Hour	10.91
Handling Rate Per Unit	$2.25

(Handling Costs Per Hour ÷ Throughput Units Per Labor Hour)

If analysis is performed at the SKU or at a customer level, a more detailed analysis is required to develop specific handling costs for a customer or a product. For example, products received in pallet quantities involve fewer labor hours than products received floor loaded, which require palletizing. Products requiring labeling also increase handling.

Investment Analysis

In this section, we consider the steps to justify an investment. There are many ways to analyze investments. Following are two methods:

• Simple Payback Period Analysis. Sometimes called the payout period method, this analysis determines the number of years that have to elapse to recover the invested capital. The formula is:

Payback Period = Capital Costs ÷ (Revenue - Expenses)

This method is useful for a quick, general analysis, but it is not exact. By itself, this measure does not indicate the desirability of a project. It calculates the time to recover capital. An alternative with a longer payback period may produce a higher return on invested capital.

• Annual Worth Method. This is an engineering economic analysis that converts cash inflows and outflows, both present and future, to their annual worth or value. If the annual worth is greater than the annual costs, the project is economically justified. When compared to other alternatives, the project with the largest positive difference between the annual worth and annual costs is most desirable. The first step is identifying the interest rate, or "cost of money." In most

Figure 4.12. Interest Table to Determine
The Capital Recovery Factor

Number of Years	Capital Recovery Factor to Find A, Given P (A = Annual Costs/P = Present Capital)						
	2% Interest	3% Interest	4% Interest	5% Interest	6% Interest	8% Interest	10% Interest
1	1.0200	1.0300	1.0400	1.0500	1.0600	1.0800	1.1000
2	0.5150	0.5226	0.5302	0.5378	0.5454	0.5608	0.5762
3	0.3468	0.3535	0.3603	0.3672	0.3741	0.2880	0.4021
4	0.2626	0.2690	0.2755	0.2820	0.2886	0.3019	0.3155
5	0.2122	0.2184	0.2246	0.2310	0.2374	0.2505	0.2638
6	0.1785	0.1846	0.1908	0.1970	0.2034	0.2163	0.2296
7	0.1545	0.1605	0.1666	0.1728	0.1791	0.1921	0.2054
8	0.1365	0.1425	0.1485	0.1547	0.1610	0.1740	0.1874
9	0.1225	0.1284	0.1345	0.1407	0.1470	0.1601	0.1736
10	0.1113	0.1172	0.1233	0.1295	0.1359	0.1490	0.1627
11	0.1022	0.1081	0.1141	0.1204	0.1268	0.1401	0.1540
12	0.0946	0.1005	0.1066	0.1128	0.1193	0.1327	0.1468
13	0.0881	0.0940	0.1001	0.1065	0.1130	0.1265	0.1408
14	0.0826	0.0885	0.0947	0.1010	0.1076	0.1213	0.1357
15	0.0778	0.0838	0.0899	0.0963	0.1030	0.1168	0.1315
16	0.0737	0.0796	0.0858	0.0923	0.0990	0.1130	0.1278
17	0.0700	0.0760	0.0822	0.0887	0.0954	0.1096	0.1247
18	0.0667	0.0727	0.0790	0.0855	0.0924	0.1067	0.1219
19	0.0638	0.0698	0.0761	0.0827	0.0896	0.1041	0.1195
20	0.0612	0.0672	0.0736	0.0802	0.0872	0.1019	0.1175
21	0.0588	0.0649	0.0713	0.0780	0.0850	0.0998	0.1156
22	0.0566	0.0627	0.0692	0.0760	0.0830	0.0980	0.1140
23	0.0547	0.0608	0.0673	0.0741	0.0813	0.0964	0.1126
24	0.0529	0.0590	0.0656	0.0725	0.0797	0.0950	0.1113
25	0.0512	0.0574	0.0640	0.0710	0.0782	0.0937	0.1102
26	0.0497	0.0559	0.0626	0.0696	0.0769	0.0925	0.1092
27	0.0483	0.0546	0.0612	0.0683	0.0757	0.0914	0.1083
28	0.0470	0.0533	0.0600	0.0671	0.0746	0.0905	0.1075
29	0.0458	0.0521	0.0589	0.0660	0.0736	0.0896	0.1067
30	0.0446	0.0510	0.0578	0.0651	0.0726	0.0888	0.1061
35	0.0400	0.0465	0.0536	0.0611	0.0690	0.0858	0.1037
40	0.0366	0.0433	0.0505	0.0583	0.0665	0.0839	0.1023
45	0.0339	0.0408	0.0483	0.0563	0.0647	0.0826	0.1014
50	0.0318	0.0389	0.0466	0.0548	0.0634	0.0817	0.1009
55	0.0301	0.0373	0.0452	0.0537	0.0625	0.0812	0.1005
60	0.0288	0.0361	0.0442	0.0528	0.0619	0.0808	0.1003
65	0.0276	0.0351	0.0434	0.0522	0.0614	0.0805	0.1002
70	0.0267	0.0343	0.0427	0.0517	0.0610	0.0804	0.1001
75	0.0259	0.0337	0.0422	0.0513	0.0608	0.0802	0.1001
80	0.0252	0.0331	0.0418	0.0510	0.0606	0.0802	0.1000
85	0.0246	0.0326	0.0415	0.0508	0.0604	0.0801	0.1000
90	0.0240	0.0323	0.0412	0.0506	0.0603	0.0801	0.1000
95	0.0236	0.0319	0.0410	0.0505	0.0602	0.0801	0.1000
100	0.0232	0.0316	0.0408	0.0504	0.0602	0.0800	0.1000
Infinite	0.0200	0.0300	0.0400	0.0500	0.0600	0.0800	0.1000

An interest table like this can be used to convert present and future worth or costs to annual worth or costs. From the first column, choose the number of years of the investment. Then, pick the factor under the correct interest rate. For example, the interest factor to convert present capital to annual costs at 3% interest over 20 years is 0.0672.

cases, it is the interest applied to the capital if it were to be invested in stocks or bonds. Relating this interest to the number of years of life in a project requires formulas to calculate the interest factors. To simplify this step, interest tables for different time intervals and interest rates have been developed. For illustrative purposes, a table (**Figure 4.12**) is provided for converting present and future worth or costs to annual worth or costs.

Some companies use their own financial tools and philosophies to compare the alternatives. For example, a large portion of the investment in AS/RS, due to the rack-supported structure, may be treated as equipment instead of being part of the building. It can be depreciated faster and may offer tax advantages. Such analysis may make this alternative economically viable. However, such detailed financial considerations are outside the scope of this publication.

Examples of Cost Analysis in the Warehouse

Example 4.1. Justifying a Single Investment

Company XYZ is considering installing an automated order selection system to improve order picking operations. Currently, manual order picking operations cost the company $125,000 per year. A new system will cost the company $800,000. It will reduce costs by 70%. The system is estimated to have a life of 30 years with annual costs for taxes and maintenance totaling $7,000. Capital is worth 8%. Determine if the project is justified.

The savings reduction in annual order picking costs is $87,500, or $125,000 x 0.70. According to **Figure 4.12**, the annual cost factor is equal to 0.0888 at 8% over 30 years. The annual costs can be calculated as follows:

Capital Recovery: Cost of System x Capital Recovery Factor = $800,000 x 0.0888 = $71,040

Taxes and Maintenance: + $7,000

Total Annual Costs: $78,040

Thus, the annual savings of $87,500 exceeds the annual costs of $78,040. From a long-range perspective, the automated order selection system would be a better investment.

Example 4.2. Comparing Alternatives, Major Foods Case Study
(Continued from Chapter 3)

Major Foods is in the process of building a new facility adjacent to an existing refrigerated facility. Space analysis has considered the following viable alternatives shown in **Figure 4.13**.

The base data in **Figure 4.14** shows the cost data associated with the different storage modules. Major Foods would like to do a cost analysis of the different storage configurations to quantitatively compare the alternatives and determine which one would provide the fastest

Figure 4.13. Space and Handling Requirements for Case Study

Type of Storage	No. of Pallets in Depth	No. of Pallets in Height	Handling Equipment Used	Time Per Pallet (Minutes)	Pallets Per Day	Time Per Day (Minutes)	Equipment Required[1]	Space Per Pallet (Sq. Ft.)
Floor	6	4	C. B. Lift Truck	3.2	1,115	3,568	8	7.1
Drive-in Racks	6	4	C. B. Lift Truck	3.3	1,115	3,680	9	7.0
Double Deep Racks	2	4	Deep Reach Lift Truck	3	1,115	3,345	8	8.4
Push-Back Racks	4	4	Reach Lift Truck	2.75	1,115	3,066	7	6.7
Push-Back Racks	2	4	Reach Lift Truck	2.75	1,115	3,066	7	8.1
Selective Racks	1	4	Reach Lift Truck	2.75	1,115	3,066	7	10.9
Selective Racks	1	10	Turret Truck (VNA)	2.4	1,115	2,676	6	3.6
			C. B. Lift Truck[2]	1.1	1,115	1,272	3	

[1] Conversion to number of pieces of equipment and workers is based on a 7.5-hr. workday.

[2] Turret trucks are not very efficient when turning into cross aisles. Thus, counterbalanced trucks will be used for pick up and drop off of pallets at the end of the very narrow aisles.

Figure 4.14. Base Data

Pallet Throughput Per Day — 1,115
Total Pallets for the Design Year — 8,411

Storage Cost Per Square Foot
Regular Building — $30
High-Bay Building with Superflat Floors — $60

Rack Cost Per Pallet
Selective Rack (4 High) — $35
Selective Rack (10 High) — $45
Double Deep Rack — $45
Drive-In Rack — $75
Push-Back Rack — $175

Cost Per Handling Unit
Counterbalanced Lift Truck — $25,000
Deep Reach Lift Truck — $30,000
Narrow Aisle Reach Truck — $28,000
Very Narrow Aisle (VNA) Turret Truck — $120,000

Cost of Special Requirements
Wire Guidance, Line Drivers — $35,000

Cost of Annual Labor Per Person — $30,000

return of its investment. Then, a qualitative analysis will be performed to further determine the best configuration for its business.

Development of Costs for Each Storage Concept. (See **Figure 4.15**.) A utilization rate was applied to the projected pallets in inventory to account for honeycombing loss. The required pallet slots (line 3) and rack cost per slot (line 4) were used to calculate rack costs. Space per pallet from **Figure 4.13** multiplied by the adjusted pallets (line 3) was used to calculate total required storage space. Incorporating an estimated cost for construction resulted in the total space cost (line 9). The VNA alternative required a higher cost per square foot because the building was higher and

Figure 4.15. Investment Per Pallet Stored for Each Storage Concept

Type of Storage	Floor	Drive-In Racks	Double Deep Racks	Push-Back Racks	Push-Back Racks	Selective Racks	Selective Racks
Handling Equipment Used	C.B. Lift Truck	C.B. Lift Truck	Deep Reach Lift Truck	Reach Lift Truck	Reach Lift Truck	Reach Lift Truck	Turret Truck (VNA)[1]
1 Design Year Pallets (Figure 4.14)	8,411	8,411	8,411	8,411	8,411	8,411	8,411
2 % Utilization (Honeycombing Loss Included)	60%	65%	80%	80%	85%	90%	90%
3 Adjusted Slots Required (Line1/Line 2)	14,018	12,940	10,514	10,514	9,895	9,346	9,346
4 Rack Cost Per Slot	$0	$75	$45	$175	$175	$35	$45
5 Total Rack Cost (Line 3 x Line 4)	$0	$970,500	$473,130	$1,839,950	$1,731,625	$327,110	$420,570
6 Space Per Pallet (Figure 4.13) in Square Feet	7.1	7.0	8.4	6.7	8.1	10.9	3.6
7 Total Storage Space (Line 6 x Line 3) in Square Feet[2]	99,528	90,580	88,318	70,444	80,150	101,871	33,646
8 Space Cost Per Square Foot	$30	$30	$30	$30	$30	$30	$60
9 Total Space Cost (Line 7 x Line 8)	$2,985,834	$2,717,400	$2,649,528	$2,113,314	$2,404,485	$3,056,142	$2,018,736
10 Number of Handling Units	8	9	8	7	7	7	6/3
11 Cost Per Handling Unit	$25,000	$25,000	$30,000	$28,000	$28,000	$28,000	$120,000/$25,000
12 Total Equipment Cost (Line 10 x Line 11)	$200,000	$225,000	$240,000	$196,000	$196,000	$196,000	$795,000
13 Cost of Special Requirements	$0	$0	$0	$0	$0	$0	$110,000
14 Total Investment (Line 5 + Line 9 + Line 12 + Line 13)	$3,185,834	$3,912,900	$3,362,658	$4,149,264	$4,332,110	$3,579,252	$3,344,306
15 Investment Per Pallet Stored (Line 14/Line 1)	$379	$465	$400	$493	$515	$426	$398

[1] Special requirements for the VNA alternative include a lift truck to transport pallets from dock pickup and drop-off stations and wire guidance.

[2] The total storage space results have been rounded for presentation in this chart. However, you will need to use the exact figures to calculate total space cost in Line 9. For example, in the first option, floor storage, total storage space is 99,527.8 (14,018 x 7.1), which is rounded to 99,528 in the chart. To calculate the total space cost, you will need to use the actual total storage space (99,527.8 x $30 = $2,985,834).

Figure 4.16. Generation of Final Alternatives

Alternative	Type of Storage	No. of Pallets In Depth	No. of Pallets In Height	No. of Pallets Stored	Investment Per Pallet Stored	Total Investment
A	Floor	6	4	2,472	$379	$936,319
	Double deep racks	2	4	1,255	$400	$501,740
	Selective racks	2	4	4,684	$426	$1,993,249
	Total			**8,411**		**$3,431,308**
B	Drive-in racks	6	4	2,472	$465	$1,150,005
	Double deep racks	2	4	1,255	$400	$501,740
	Selective racks	1	4	4,684	$426	$1,993,249
	Total			**8,411**		**$3,644,994**
C	Push-back racks	4	4	2,472	$493	$1,219,472
	Push-back racks	2	4	1,255	$515	$646,391
	Selective racks	1	4	4,684	$426	$1,993,249
	Total			**8,411**		**$3,859,112**
D	Double deep racks	2	4	6,781	$400	$2,710,996
	Selective racks	1	4	1,630	$426	$693,637
	Total			**8,411**		**$3,404,633**
E	Selective racks	1	10	**8,411**	$398	**$3,344,306**

needed a superflat floor. Special requirements included the need for wire guidance and counterbalanced lift trucks with the VNA alternative. Line 14 shows the total investment if only one type of storage module is used. Investment per pallet stored represents the capital costs.

Development and Evaluation of the Final Alternatives. The capital costs for each storage concept were calculated. Depending on the inventory profile, different concepts could be used for different types of SKUs. SKUs with an average of over 20 pallets of inventory were placed in 6-deep storage on the floor. SKUs in the range of six to 11 pallets in inventory were slotted for double deep racks. The balance of the pallets was to be serviced by a reach lift truck in selective racks. In total, five alternatives were generated as shown in **Figure 4.16**.

Figure 4.17 summarizes the next step, which was an investment analysis using the payback period method. Alternative E, which had the lowest capital investment, was used as the base alternative. Although Alternatives B & C had lower operating costs, they required a substantially higher capital investment than E. The relative payback period was 10 and 8 years respectively, which made them less appealing to management. Alternative A involved three different types of modules. Management agreed that this made it less flexible and more difficult to manage and operate than D or E. The choice was narrowed down to D and E. Alternative D required more capital than E but was less expensive to operate. It was necessary to examine each alternative in qualitative terms before a final selection was made.

Alternative D:

• Is preferred by workers and supervisors who are more accustomed to working with this equipment.

Figure 4.17. Economic Summary

	A	B	C	D	E
Type of Storage	Floor	Drive-in Racks	Push-Back Racks	Double Deep Racks	Selective Racks
	Double Deep Racks	Double Deep Racks	Push-Back Racks	Selective Racks	VNA
	Selective Racks	Selective Racks	Selective Racks		
Total Investment	$3,431,308	$3,644,994	$3,859,112	$3,404,633	$3,344,306
Difference from Base	$87,002	$300,688	$514,806	$60,327	base
Annual Operating Costs[1]	$240,000	$240,000	$210,000	$240,000	$270,000
Difference from Base	($30,000)	($30,000)	($60,000)	($30,000)	base
Relative Payback Period (Years)	3	10	9	2	—

[1] Annual operating costs are estimated from labor costs based on the number of handling units required.

- Is easier for order picking, as it has wider aisles and picking and storage vehicles can pass each other. This is not possible in Alternative E, where the aisles are only six feet wide.

- For the future, a conventional height facility may be easier to sell than one that is 50 feet high.

Alternative E:

- Uses only selective rack, which provides better accessibility to individual pallets.

Selection of the Preferred Alternative. For the new warehouse, management decided to pursue Alternative D based on the quantitative and qualitative analysis.

FOOTNOTES & REFERENCES

Chapter 2 — Warehouse Time Standards

[1] No author, *VBA Work Measurement System and Work Rate Standards*, Veterans Benefits Administration, Dept. of Veterans Affairs, Circular 20-00-2, Sept. 2000.

[2] Dossett, Royal, "Work-Measured Labor Standards: The State of the Art," *Industrial Engineering*, April 1995, p.21.

[3] Gagnon, Eugene, *Using Work Measurement for Warehouse Management*, Warehousing Education and Research Council, 1993, p.8.

[4] Dosset, *loc. cit.*, p.22.

[5] Barnes, Ralph, *Motion and Time Study Design and Measurement of Work*, 7th ed., John Wiley & Sons, 1980, p.406.

[6] Derived from Barnes, *loc. cit.,* p.437.

Chapter 3 — Warehouse Space Calculations

[1] McKnight, Douglas, "A Practical Guide to Evaluating the Functional Utility of Warehouses," *The Appraisal Journal*, January 1999, p.30.

[2] Templer, Audrey, "Creating a Safe Loading Dock," *Plant Engineering*, April 1994, p.86.

[3] Freese, Thomas, "The Dock: Your Warehouse's Most Valuable Real Estate," *Material Handling Management*, June 2000, p.98.

[4] McKnight, *loc. cit.*, p.30.

[5] For more information on simulation and its application to warehousing problems, refer to *Using Modeling to Solve Warehousing Problems*, Warehousing Education and Research Council, 1998.

[6] Sweitlik, Walt, "Instead of Loading Dock, Think Material Transfer Zone," *Plant Engineering*, December 2002, p.38.

[7] Freese, *loc. cit.*, p.98.

[8] No author, "Dock Doors Get Groceries Moving," *Modern Materials Handling*, Mid-October 2002, p.59.

[9] Freese, *loc. cit.,* p.100.

[10] No author, *Using Modeling to Solve Warehousing Problems*, Warehousing Education and Research Council, 1998.

[11] Refer to *Using Modeling to Solve Warehousing Problems*, Warehousing Education and Research Council, 1998, p.100.

Chapter 4 — Warehouse Cost Calculations

[1] Based on Warehouse Cost Models discussion from *Using Modeling to Solve Warehousing Problems*, Warehousing Education and Research Council, pp.33–37.

[2] Speh, Thomas, *A Model for Determining Total Warehousing Costs: For Private, Public and Contract Warehouses*, Warehousing Education and Research Council, 1990.

[3] No author, *2002 Warehousing Salaries and Wages*, Warehousing Education and Research Council, 2002.

REFERENCES

Airtrax Inc., Hammonton, NJ. (609) 567-7800. www.airtrax.com.

Consulting Services Company, a division of Bohm Company, Chicago, IL. (312) 944-1787. www.bohmco.com.

Crown Equipment Corporation, New Bremen, OH. (419) 629-2311. www.crown.com.

Hyster Company, Greenville, NC. (800) 497-8371. www.hysterusa.com

Landoll Corporation, Marysville, KS. (785) 562-5381. www.landoll.com.

Rite-Hite Corporation, Milwaukee, WI. (800) 285-5956. www.ritehite.com.

Raymond of New Jersey LLC, Union, NJ. (607) 656-2311. www.raymondcorp.com.

White Systems Inc., Kenilworth, NJ. (908) 272-6700. www.whitesystems.com.

GLOSSARY

ABC (Activity-Based Costing) — A method of allocating costs associated with products and services by identifying discrete, quantifiable activities or work units with assigned costs.

Address — A number or combination of numbers and/or letters used to designate a particular warehouse location, facing, or slot.

AEI (Automatic Equipment Identification) — The use of machine-readable tags on equipment such as railcars, containers, and trucks to track location and usage.

AGV (Automated Guided Vehicle) — A vehicle equipped with automatic guidance equipment, either electromagnetic or optical, which is capable of following prescribed guide paths. AGVs may be equipped for vehicle programming and stop selection, blocking, and any other special functions required by the system.

Aisle — Any passageway within a storage area.

> **Cross Aisle** — A passageway at right angles to main aisles and access aisles, used for the movement of supplies, equipment, and personnel.

> **Fire Aisle** — A passageway established to aid in escaping, fighting, or preventing the spread of fire, or for access to firefighting equipment.

> **Main Aisle** — A passageway to permit the flow of equipment, supplies, and personnel; it generally runs the length of the building and is wide enough to permit vehicles to pass.

ANSI (American National Standards Institute) — An organization dedicated to the establishment of a wide range of standards for industrial environments.

ASN (Advance Shipment Notice) — A document, usually transmitted electronically by a shipper, containing detailed information about the contents of a shipment and made available to the recipient anticipating its arrival.

AS/RS (Automated Storage/Retrieval System) — A combination of equipment and controls that handles, stores, and retrieves materials with precision, accuracy, and speed under a defined degree of automation. Systems vary from relatively simple order picking machines operating in small storage structures to large, computer-controlled storage/retrieval systems totally integrated into the manufacturing and distribution process.

Average Performance Index — The ratio of the total standard time to the actual number of available labor hours.

Barcode — An arrangement of rectangular bars and spaces in a defined pattern that represents specific alphanumeric information. Two- and three-dimensional barcodes follow the same concept but have the capacity to store more information.

Barcode Scanner — An instrument that uses reflected light technology to read information from a barcoded label and transmits that information to other devices for processing.

Benchmarking — The practice of comparing specific measures of performance of an organization against the performance of other comparable organizations in an effort to increase efficiency, enhance productivity, and improve profitability.

Bins — Containers used to store small stockkeeping units.

Bulk Stack — Storage of large quantities of material on the floor in stacked unit loads. Also known as deep floor storage.

CAD (Computer Aided Design) — Computer drafting software used in the process of developing, producing, and evaluating designs.

Cantilever Rack — A structural framework in which the product rests on arms supported at one end by uprights providing continuous shelving without vertical separations. Used for storing long units, such as pipes and rolled carpets.

Capacity Planning and Scheduling — A process for determining the labor and equipment capacity required to meet operating schedules within the limits of current resources.

Carousel Storage System — A continuous automated storage loop, either vertical or horizontal, which indexes storage containers brought to the picker or replenisher at one end of the loop.

Clear Height — The distance measured from the floor to the lowest overhead obstruction. See Working Headroom.

Constraints — Limitations of a set of criteria.

Conveyor — Powered or gravity-driven devices that move loads over a fixed path.

Counterbalanced Lift Truck — A lift truck with weight mounted on its rear in order to offset the weight of the load.

Crane — An overhead device used to lift and transport material within a fixed area.

Cross Docking — A process in which product is received in a facility, occasionally married with other products going to the same destination, then shipped at the earliest opportunity, without going into long-term storage. The process requires advance knowledge of the inbound product, its destination, and a system for routing the product to the proper outbound vehicle.

CRP (Continuous Replenishment Planning) — A method of transferring responsibility for the replenishment of a retailer's warehouse from the retailer to suppliers.

CTR (Computerized Truck Routing) — A method of using computers to generate truck routes based on stops, delivery appointments, and backhauls to improve utilization.

Cube — Volume of an item. Cube is calculated by multiplying the length, width, and height of an item.

Cycle Counting — A method of taking physical inventory in which only a percentage of items are counted at a time but eventually all inventory is counted.

Demurrage — A charge against a receiver as a penalty for the detention of a carrier's equipment beyond the period of time allowed for loading or unloading.

DOS (Disk Operating System) — An older generation of programming software built into a disk or a computer system that initiates, sets up, controls, and manages a computer's operation. It is primarily characterized by the use of text in carrying out instructions to the computer — as opposed to the more current Windows, which uses icons or symbols in a graphical user interface (GUI).

Drive-In Rack — A structural framework that is open at the front and blocked at the back with cross bracing. The shelves consist of rails connected to the uprights. Unit loads may be placed in two or more rows deep by entering the rack from the front and driving the lift truck between the rails. Careful consideration should be given to unit load clearance requirements, both vertical and horizontal.

Drive-Through Rack — These are similar to drive-in racks except that the cross bracing is distributed across the top of the rack structure, thus permitting the lift truck to drive through the rack structure from one end to the other.

DRP (Distribution Requirements Planning) — A management process for determining inventory needs to ensure that supply sources are able to meet demand requirements.

DSD (Direct to Store Delivery) — A distribution methodology in which a supplier delivers directly to the retail outlet, without going through the retailer's distribution center.

Dual Cycle — The strategy of using radio frequency (RF) technology to improve productivity by assigning lift truck drivers tasks on their return trips so as not to travel back without a load or task. For example, if a driver takes a pallet from the docks to storage, then his or her RF terminal should query the warehouse management system for another task nearby, such as taking material from storage to the docks. Dual cycling can increase a lift truck's throughput by 30% to 50% (i.e., from 15 pallet moves per hour to 20). Also known as interleaving.

ECR (Efficient Consumer Response) — The grocery industry's acronym for QR (Quick Response), which promotes the development of a demand-driven grocery supply system in which partners work together to streamline business processes to provide more consumer value at a lower cost.

EDI (Electronic Data Interchange) — The electronic (computer to computer), paperless exchange of business data between locations, using a standardized data format.

Ergonomics — The study of humans and their interaction with their surroundings, using concepts in the physical sciences and engineering to design working environments that reduce fatigue and stress while increasing productivity and enhancing worker safety.

ESFR (Early Suppression Fast Response) — A ceiling-based high-density fire protection system used as an alternative to in-rack sprinkler systems. This system uses overhead sprinkler heads, which release tremendous amounts of water.

Facilities Planning — The process of laying out a facility to show the arrangement of equipment, material flows, and other elements to establish a safe and efficient working environment.

Facility Location Analysis — A study that determines the best location(s) for a facility within a network of supply and demand, with the objective of either lowering transportation and operating costs or maintaining and improving customer service. Frequently, the solution involves a compromise of both.

Facing — The position in a block or rack occupied by a warehousing unit from which a worker can access a product.

FIFO (First In/First Out) — An inventory control requirement to ship the oldest lot of an item in the warehouse first.

Fixed Slot — A slot reserved for a specific stockkeeping unit. (For dedicated storage systems.)

Floating Slot — A slot that becomes available for any stockkeeping unit as soon as it is empty. (For random storage systems.)

Floor Load — The weight that the floor can safely support, designated by pounds per square foot.

G&A (General & Administrative) — The people and activities of a company that support its overall mission and which are not directly related to the operation of a specific warehouse. For a company operating multiple warehouses, the closure of one warehouse will not necessarily affect general administrative functions.

GMA Pallet — A pallet that adheres to published performance specifications established by the Grocery Manufacturers' Association (GMA). These specifications include exact dimensions of 48 inches x 40 inches with a platform height not exceeding 6 inches.

Golden Zone — The set of facings that are most accessible to pickers. The most popular, fastest-moving items are usually slotted in the golden zone.

HAZMAT (Hazardous Materials) — Raw materials and products that have been classified by regulatory agencies as dangerous — i.e., flammable, toxic, caustic, etc.

Honeycombing — The wasted space brought about by partially filled rows and stacks.

ILM (Integrated Logistics Management) — The coordination of logistics functions and collaboration of supply chain participants to produce total system efficiencies.

In-Transit Inventory — Product that has not reached its final destination but is still a saleable asset.

JIT (Just In Time) — A technique of replenishing an operation (manufacturing, retail, etc.) with materials just before they are needed.

LAN (Local Area Network) — Software and wiring systems used to connect computers and peripheral devices in order to share information and resources.

LED (Light Emitting Diode) — A device that discharges light using a solid-state unidirectional conductor.

Let Down — Lowering a unitized load from its position in a stack or storage rack to a location where partial withdrawals can be made (e.g., forward pick areas).

LIFO (Last In/First Out) — An inventory control requirement that the newest lot of an item that enters the warehouse is the first one to leave.

Line — A single item of inventory separately identified on a customer order, regardless of quantity.

Locator System — A system that records and tracks the exact location of all stockkeeping units in the warehouse.

Logistics Supply Chain — The collection of functions and activities that involve the acquisition, transport, storage, distribution, handling, and management of a product or service from the source of creation or supply to the demand points.

Lot — A subdivision of a stockkeeping unit used to provide specific identity to a quantity of product with unique characteristics such as expiration date, production run, or specific ingredient contents.

LTL (Less-Than-Truckload) — Mode of transportation where multiple shipments are combined on one truck. Generally it is slower and more expensive than truckload shipments.

MHIA (Material Handling Institute of America) — A professional organization dedicated to disseminating information and researching material handling issues.

Microsoft Excel — A popular spreadsheet program. It is used as a database for information and as a medium to relate an almost unlimited number of records in a format of rows and columns, which can be translated into charts and graphs.

Model — A representation of an actual system. This representation would capture most of the key data elements, relationships, tasks, and constraints found in the real system and allow the analyst to test alternatives on paper or on the computer without affecting the real system. It is used to make comparisons of alternatives or to determine feasibility.

Moving Beam Scanner — A noncontact barcode reader that dynamically searches for barcodes by sweeping a moving optical beam (usually a laser beam) through a field of view. This type of scanner is used when packages are moving at high speeds and when handheld scanners are impractical. This type of scanner eliminates the need for an operator.

NIOSH (National Institute for Occupational Safety and Health) — A government agency dedicated to the monitoring and control of safety and health issues in the workplace.

OA (Operating Administration) — The group of people and activities that manage and control the operations of a specific facility. If the facility is closed, then this function disappears with it.

Operations Research — A scientific approach to managerial decision making, it applies mathematical models and the use of computers to study difficult and unstructured problems. Also known as management science.

Optimum — The best overall result that can be obtained from a system. There will probably be sub-optimization of some components of the system, but the overall system will be the most effective.

Order Picker — A person who works in the warehouse with the responsibility of collecting the correct quantity of the correct item from a designated location. Also known as order selector.

Pallet Overhang — The portion of a pallet that extends beyond rack beams into the aisle or the back of the rack.

Pallet Pattern — The arrangement of the items in a unitized load. Also known as unit load pattern.

PDT (Predetermined Time Standards) — A collection of time values developed by experienced time analysts who agreed on basic factors, concepts, and constraints underlying their system.

Pick Line — An arrangement of stockkeeping units in some orderly system to facilitate selecting or picking items to satisfy orders.

Pick-To-Light — A technology that uses electronic devices such as light-emitting diodes (LEDs) and liquid crystal displays (LCDs) on the pick line to show pickers the correct item and sometimes the correct quantity to include in an order.

Portable Data Terminals — Devices used to gather operating information. They communicate with the host computer by radio frequency signals or by batch downloads at a central site. Also known as radio frequency terminals.

POS (Point of Sale) — Information that is captured by devices as the sale is made; the data is then distributed to sales, inventory, and financial management systems.

Product Overhang — The condition created when the unitized product overhangs the pallet or platform surface.

Product Underhang — The condition resulting when a load is smaller than the pallet or platform surface on which the product is laid.

Programming — A set of instructions written in a specific language and using specific syntax developed for the computer in order to accomplish a task or calculation.

Push-Back Racks — Structural frameworks that go more than one pallet deep. Unit loads are placed on rails and are "pushed back" to accommodate more pallets in front. Because the oldest product is pushed to the back and a newer load is placed in front, it is not recommended for FIFO movement of small lots.

QR (Quick Response) — See ECR (Efficient Consumer Response).

Racks — Metal framework upon which units or unitized loads are placed. See cantilever rack, drive-in rack, drive-through rack, and selective pallet rack.

Rack Slot — The position occupied by a warehousing unit in a rack. The slot may be one or more units high, or one or more units deep. Rack slots may be fixed or floating.

Rack Unit Clearance — Space allowed for handling clearance between warehousing units stored in racks.

Random Seed — A controlling entity used to generate a set of random numbers in a simulation program.

Reach Lift Truck — This truck can operate efficiently in aisles as narrow as 8 feet and can lift loads to a height of about 32 feet. It uses a pantograph reach mechanism or moving mast to extend the forks to move pallets. It is widely used for pallet handling.

Rewarehousing — The practice of rehandling material to create storage space or to consolidate like stockkeeping units.

RFDC (Radio Frequency Data Collection) — The wireless transfer of data between a data collection device, such as a barcode scanner, and a data processing device or controller. Sometimes the controller can transmit signals back to the data collection device, thus providing feedback to the data collector.

RFID (Radio Frequency Identification) — This system employs identification tags with imbedded microchips that are either programmed or reprogrammable. They emit signals that uniquely identify them and can be tracked using signal sensors.

SCM (Supply Chain Management) — The practice of integrating processes to optimize product and information flow from the purchase of raw materials to the delivery of the finished product.

Selective Pallet Rack — The term used to designate one-deep shelf type racks. Originally designed for pallets, it is also used for storage of large units. The racks consist of uprights and beams and may be fixed or adjustable. Racks may be bolted to the floor or walls. When the racks are positioned back to back, they are secured to each other with space bars or spacer rods. Beams may be designed to accept decking or cross bracing to prevent loads from falling. Also known as a single deep pallet rack.

Shelving — Wood or metal boards fixed horizontally and supported by frames or uprights. Shelving may be fixed or adjustable. Used for small quantities or broken cases.

Simulation — The process of representing a system through the development of a mathematical model and testing the model's performance under different operating scenarios. This exercise tests the effectiveness and functionality of a proposed system before it is physically implemented. Simulation is able to identify potential areas for system breakdowns and can point out the changes and improvements required to improve performance or prevent failures.

Site Selection — The process of determining the best location for a new facility based on qualitative and quantitative evaluations of alternative sites.

Six Sigma — Statistical term defining standards with only 3.4 errors or defects per million measurable units of product or service.

SKU (Stockkeeping Unit) — A warehousing item that must be stored and accounted for separately. A single stockkeeping unit may have to be stored in different lots for the purpose of quality control, maintaining stock rotation, isolation, or quarantine.

Slot — See Facing.

Spreadsheet — This is a form characterized by a configuration of rows and columns containing mathematical expressions, raw data, logical expressions, text, etc.

Stack — The positioning of two or more items on top of each other.

Stackability — The ability of a load to sustain the weight of one or more loads when stacked.

Stacking Height — The number of unit loads (e.g., pallets) that can be stacked on top of each other efficiently without the danger of the stack falling.

SQC (Statistical Quality Control) — Mathematical tool that sheds light on process variation by tracking and predicting trends.

Storage Module — A single storage unit, which might have the capacity to hold multiple inventory units.

Tactical Planning — This involves the identification of the best configuration of facility, equipment, personnel, and other resources required to fulfill a warehouse's mission. It is characterized by shorter planning horizons than strategic planning.

Third Party — A company that provides services for clients. These services may include warehousing, transportation, customer service, manipulation of merchandise, and any other client requirements. Also known as outsourcing.

Tier — A single layer of units forming part of a unit load.

TQM (Total Quality Management) — The concept of continuous improvement to develop processes that are controlled and result in products of predictable quality.

Turret Truck — A lift truck that operates in aisles as narrow as 6 feet and can lift loads to a height of over 40 feet. The truck does not turn in the storage aisles, but the fork mechanism on the masts can turn ninety degrees left or right to store or remove pallets from either side.

Unit Clearance — Space allowed for handling clearance between columns or stacks, or between tiers in racks, shelves, or bins.

UPC (Universal Product Code) — A standard barcode symbology used in retail businesses, particularly in the grocery industry.

UCC 128 — A standard barcode symbology with defined data elements.

Validate — The process of verifying information against a known set of data in a model to ensure an accurate representation.

Value Engineering — This involves replacing high-cost components with more economical options that can lower costs without compromising a system's efficiency.

VNA (Very Narrow Aisle) — A storage aisle of at least five feet in width for turret trucks.

Voice-Directed Picking — A picking system in which pickers are directed to the proper pick aisle, item to pick, quantity to pick, and more by voice commands transmitted via radio frequency directly to their headphones. Pick list information from the warehouse management system is translated from programming code to voice commands that can be spoken in any language preferred (English, Spanish, French, etc.). Voice-directed picking frees a picker's hand for picking and eliminates manual reading errors.

Wand Scanner — A handheld scanning device used as a contact barcode reader. It is shaped like an oversized pen and the operator guides it across the barcode. Also known as a light pen.

Windows Environment — A type of operating system that helps control and manage software programs in the computer. It is primarily characterized by using icons and symbols in a graphical menu — as opposed to DOS, which uses text. Also known as Windows.

WMS (Warehouse Management System) — Computer software for managing and tracking the activity of products, equipment, and people through the warehouse. The system may interface with barcode and radio frequency technology to gather and communicate information.

Working Clearance — The space allowed between the top of a stack or column and the lowest overhead obstruction, such as ceiling joists, beams, sprinkler heads, or steam pipes. It provides space for the load to be lifted off the supporting structure and for fire suppression systems to operate effectively. This allowance will vary depending on local fire codes.

Working Headroom — The distance measured from the floor to a point twelve inches or more below the lowest overhead obstructions (see Working Clearance). Working headroom is usually controlled to avoid coming into contact with overhead obstructions in the storage area and to maintain the unit clearances required by local fire regulations or ordinances. Same as clear height.

Definitions from this glossary came from the authors and the following other sources:

Curt, Barry, "Are Warehouse Management Systems Right For You?" *Operations and Fulfillment*, May/June 1997, p. 121.

Guidelines to the Integration of Bar Code Scanning with Unit Load Packaging Conveying, Integrated Systems and Controls Council, a council of the Material Handling Industry of America, 1993.

Industrial Engineering Terminology, McGraw-Hill Inc. and the Institute of Industrial Engineers, 1991.

Napolitano, Maida, *Making the Move to Cross Docking*, Warehousing Education and Research Council, 2000.

Napolitano, Maida, *Using Modeling to Solve Warehousing Problems*, Warehousing Education and Research Council, 1998.

BIBLIOGRAPHY

Chapter 2 — Warehouse Time Standards

No author, *Standardization of Work Measurement: Defense Work Measurement Standard Time Data Program*, DoD 5010.15.1-M, January 1977.

No author, *VBA Work Measurement System and Work Rate Standards*, Veterans Benefits Administration, Dept. of Veterans Affairs, Circular 20-00-2, September 2000.

Aichlmayr, Mary, "Add a Kicker to Warehouse ROI," *Transportation & Distribution*, January 2002, pp.39–43.

Barnes, Ralph, *Motion and Time Study Design and Measurement of Work*, 7th ed., John Wiley & Sons, 1980.

Dossett, Royal, "Work-Measured Labor Standards: The State of the Art," *Industrial Engineering*, April 1995, pp.21–25.

Gagnon, Eugene, *Using Work Measurement for Warehouse Management*, Warehousing Education and Research Council, 1993.

Koepfer, Chris, "Automating Time Studies," *Modern Machine Shop*, September 2002, p.60.

Mason, Sarah, "Work Measurement Tools: Buyer's Guide," *IIE Solutions*, March 2002, pp.51–57.

Napolitano, Maida, *Using Modeling to Solve Warehousing Problems*, Warehousing Education and Research Council, 1998.

Trunk, Christopher, "Pick-to-Light: Choices, Choices, Choices," *Material Handling Engineering*, September 1998, pp.44–48.

Trunk, Christopher, "Warehouse Management Systems: New Pathways to Justification," *Material Handling Engineering*, January 1998, pp.48–60.

Chapter 3 — Warehouse Space Calculations

No author, "Dock Doors Get Groceries Moving," *Modern Materials Handling*, Mid-October 2002, p.59.

Frazelle, Edward H. and James Apple, Jr., "Materials Handling Technologies," *The Logistics Handbook*, The Free Press, 1994, pp.547–603.

Freese, Thomas, "The Dock: Your Warehouse's Most Valuable Real Estate," *Material Handling Management*, June 2000, pp.97–101.

Hare, Bob, "Are Your Dock Doors Hindering Plant Productivity?" *Plant Engineering*, August 2001, pp.38–40.

McKnight, Douglas, "A Practical Guide to Evaluating the Functional Utility of Warehouses," *The Appraisal Journal*, January 1999, p.30.

Napolitano, Maida, *Using Modeling to Solve Warehousing Problems*, Warehousing Education and Research Council, 1998.

Richardson, Helen, "Design Warehouses for Flexibility," *Transportation & Distribution*, October 1998, pp.119–123.

Saenz, Norman, Jr., "Four Walls, No Windows," *Operations & Fulfillment*, October 2001, pp.110–116.

Silverman, Robert and Sisko, M. Geoffrey, "Maximizing Space — A Key to Productivity," *Warehousing Forum*, December 2002.

Sweitlik, Walt, "Instead of Loading Dock, Think Material Transfer Zone," *Plant Engineering*, December 2002, pp.36–40.

Templer, Audrey, "Creating a Safe Loading Dock," *Plant Engineering*, April 1994, pp.86–90.

Tompkins, James, et al., *Facilities Planning*, 2nd ed., John Wiley & Sons, 1996.

Chapter 4 — Warehouse Cost Calculations

No author, *2002 Warehousing Salaries and Wages*, Warehousing Education and Research Council, 1998.

Aichlmayr, Mary, "Add a Kicker to Warehouse ROI," *Transportation and Distribution*, January 2002, pp.39–43.

Balboni, Barbara (Senior Editor), *RS Means Square Foot Costs — 23rd Annual Edition*, R. S. Means Co. Inc., 2002.

Napolitano, Maida, *Making the Move to Cross Docking*, Warehousing Education and Research Council, 2000.

Napolitano, Maida, *Using Modeling to Solve Warehousing Problems*, Warehousing Education and Research Council, 1998.

Sisko, M. Geoffrey, and Gross & Associates, *Rules of Thumb for Warehousing and Distribution Equipment Costs*, Gross & Associates, 2003.

Speh, Thomas, *A Model for Determining Total Warehousing Costs: For Private, Public and Contract Warehouses*, Warehousing Education and Research Council, 1998.

Trunk, Christopher, "Warehouse Management Systems: New Pathways to Justification," *Material Handling Engineering*, January 1998, pp.48–55.